Pi

PERMISSION
TO
CARE

"I have been a pharmacist and leader in healthcare for several years, and I know the importance of creating a culture that values empathy, adaptability, and meaningful connections with patients and coworkers. Cory helps both the individual healthcare provider and leader achieve this while finding joy in their work. This book can help set you and your healthcare team up for success."

—**JOSHUA CARZOLI,** PharmD, MBA, BCACP,
Community Health Center Chief Operating Officer

"As a humor expert, I understand the importance and value of incorporating comedy in the workplace. Even when the workplace is healthcare, the skills of improv and humor remain. In *Permission to Care,* Cory gives you the prescription for the practical application of improv comedy to create a more effective healthcare culture."

—**ANDREW TARVIN,** Humor Expert, Bestselling Author of *Humor That Works: The Missing Skill for Success and Happiness at Work*

"You might be the most clinically sound, evidence-based practitioner in the world. But if you can't communicate your knowledge with patients and providers, then you're lessening your ability to make an impact in healthcare and to advance in your career. That's where Cory comes in. He'll give you the skills to provide empathetic, compassionate, and effective care while creating a workplace culture that you'll actually enjoy."

—**BRANDON DYSON,** PharmD, BCOP,
BCPS, Founder of tl;dr Pharmacy

"I have worked and interacted with thousands of pharmacists and student pharmacists, and I know that despite their dedication to learning the hard skills needed, many enter the workforce lacking the adaptability, empathy, and mindset needed to thrive in healthcare. Cory helps create the bridge between the hard and soft skills needed to be a well-rounded healthcare professional. This book, filled with stories that will make readers laugh and self-reflect, can help set healthcare professionals and their organizations up for success in an ever-turbulent healthcare environment."

—**TIM ULBRICH,** PharmD, Cofounder and CEO of Your Financial Pharmacist, Coauthor of *Seven Figure Pharmacist*

"And I heard a voice cry out in the Arizona desert, 'Make straight the way of improv in healthcare.' Dr. Cory Jenks is that voice. The healthcare system is broken, so Cory decided to throw improv comedy at it. The results couldn't be more unexpected. What I loved about this book is that it rightly points out the careless nature of healthcare and provides realistic solutions for individuals and teams to implement and improve patient care experiences. My hope is that you'll read this book and experience the power and benefits of 'Yes, And' for your patients and healthcare teams."

—**ALEX BARKER,** PharmD, Founder of The Happy PharmD, Author of *Indispensable: The Prescription for a Fulfilling Pharmacy Career*

"Applying the principles of improvisational comedy to fix the ailing healthcare system?! What kind of nonsense is this pharmacist dispensing?! Or is he on to something? Cory Jenks has the remedy to treat the chronic stress and frustration of healthcare and provide good health and joy for patients and healthcare professionals alike. And he can even read my scribbled prescriptions! What a guy!"

—**BRAD NIEDER,** MD, The Healthy Humorist®

"As the founder of an improv theater and someone who specializes in leadership development, I have seen the transformation in thousands of people and business cultures in my twelve years of experience. Cory is the perfect person to take these transformative skills and combine them with his decade-long career as a pharmacist to help improve one of our nation's greatest problems: healthcare. *Permission to Care* is the elixir to fix what ails a you, the burnt-out healthcare practitioner. Through real life experience and an entertaining style, this book will have you *aspirin*-g to new frontiers in your career."

—**JUSTIN LUKASEWICZ,** Owner and Executive
Producer of Tucson Improv Movement

PERMISSION

TO

BUILDING A HEALTHCARE CULTURE THAT THRIVES IN CHAOS

CORY JENKS, PharmD

Published by Mandala Tree Press
www.mandalatreepress.com

Paperback ISBN: 9781954801301
Hardcover with Dust Jacket ISBN: 9781954801318
Case Laminate Hardcover ISBN: 9781954801349
eBook ISBN: 9781954801325

MED035000   MEDICAL / Health Care Delivery
MED024000   MEDICAL / Education & Training
MED034000   MEDICAL / Healing

Cover design by Scott Graham
Edited by Catherine Christensen, Justin Greer, and Valene Wood
Typeset by Kaitlin Barwick

www.coryjenks.com

To our patients who trust us with their health:
Let this book remind us to treat you
like the human beings you are.

To Poppa, my first dedicated "glob" reader:
If only you could see what your little shit
wrote now. I promise, I am having fun.

And to my boys:
Remember to always keep playing.
Except right now, because it's past your
bedtime, and you need to go to sleep so
Daddy can finish writing this book.

Contents

CONTENTS

FIND HAPPINESS
IN HEALTHCARE

Admit it. You aren't so sure about this book. A book written by a pharmacist, who also is an improv comedian, on how applying the lessons of improv can make our healthcare experience better? On the surface it seems like a Mad Libs story gone horribly wrong:

> *Okay, I need a healthcare professional that gets less respect than a doctor but also doesn't have to touch bodily fluids or holes.*
>
> *Can't be a nurse, lots of fluids and holes for them. An audiologist technically does go into a body hole, so they're out. Oh, let's go with a pharmacist—the Rodney Dangerfield of healthcare. The only bodily fluid they have to deal with are their own tears after a fourteen-hour shift with no lunch break.*
>
> *Great, now I need something you experiment with in college, but let's challenge ourselves, so no drugs or sex stuff.*

My roommate got caught up in an improv troupe
the fall semester of sophomore year. He spoke in nothing
but puns until spring break.
Bingo.

I'd like to challenge you. Challenge you to read on. Challenge you to change your mindset on how to solve our myriad healthcare issues. Challenge you to say yes to a different spin on the seemingly never-ending pursuit of providing the type of healthcare our patients deserve while creating an environment that healthcare professionals actually want to work in. You may not believe improv can be a solution to our healthcare woes—yet—but at least it's not going to hurt! The last time I checked, the most common complaint about our healthcare system *isn't* that there is too much comedy going around.

And there *is* plenty to complain and be concerned about when it comes to being a healthcare professional. Our providers are burning out at high rates. One study showed burnout rates as high as 66 percent among my fellow clinical pharmacists.[1] How much does it cost an organization to replace a burned-out pharmacist? What is the cost in safety to a patient for a provider who is burned out? How about the cost in life satisfaction for a healthcare professional who is burned out? These are questions that we wouldn't need to answer so often if we could instill skills in our organizations and healthcare professionals that kept them from burning

---

1. Hagemann, TM, Reed, BN, Bradley, BA, et al. "Burnout among clinical pharmacists: Causes, interventions, and a call to action." *Journal of the American College of Clinical Pharmacy.* 2020; 3: 832–842.

out. I know from experience that applying improv skills has helped me navigate my own path away from burnout.

What about healthcare's other problems, like medical errors? Well, the price tag on that issue here in the USA is a cool $20 billion—almost as much as the entire GDP of Iceland. And while the sticker shock of our medical errors will make you want to run all the way to Reykjavík, what should really make you cringe is the literal human cost of medical errors. That grim toll is approximately 100,000 people dying each year, or about 274 every single day.[2] Nobody has that many enemies, so that means it's *also* our family and friends who are dying—and none of them, enemies included, deserve the fate of being killed by the very system they trust to heal them. Improv teaches many skills that can help with both burnout and medical errors, such as better communication, empathy, and keeping providers invested.

I do appreciate your skepticism and that you are still reading. You wouldn't be a discerning provider or patient of healthcare if you weren't wary of the many so-called solutions and fixes we have tried to tame the ever-growing frustrations and costs we face in caring for our sick. Yet I promise you that if you stay with me, by the end of this book you will know how applying the skills, mindset, and philosophy of improv comedy can help mend the gaping wounds of our healthcare system. Improv can create a better experience for patients and providers, and you will be excited to put them into practice yourself.

2. Rodziewicz TL, Houseman B, Hipskind JE. Medical Error Reduction and Prevention. [Updated 2021 Aug 6]. In: StatPearls [Internet]. Treasure Island (FL): StatPearls Publishing; 2021 Jan-. Available from: https://www.ncbi.nlm.nih.gov/books/NBK499956/

Chapter 1

DITCH THE SCRIPT

For a Happier Healthcare Experience

Working in healthcare was supposed to be noble. Don your white coat, scrubs, and face mask and jump into the profession of saving lives. That's what we are told. That's what we think when we decide to dedicate decades of our lives training so that we can be the healers of our friends, family, and community. There are long nights in the library studying, memorizing chemical structures, and digesting and regurgitating guideline after guideline.

It's grueling, unforgiving work.

The payoff is what makes it all worth it, right? At least that's what we tell ourselves to get through the missed birthdays, the forgone relationships, and the carelessness of our young adulthood. Because someday that payoff is going to make all this sacrifice worth it.

There'll be a steady job, respect from others—and the paycheck ain't nothing to sneeze at either. You'll be dedicating your life to saving and caring for others. What could be more noble?

At least, in your mind that's what healthcare is supposed to be: empathetic interactions, taking care of patients, and working together in a healthcare team dedicated to improving health outcomes. You did all of that studying, memorizing, and factoid regurgitation to be ready to fix people.

Except, from day one, you step into a coldly indifferent healthcare environment that doesn't care how many times you can recite the Krebs cycle. It doesn't care about your ideals, your vision for healthcare, or the crushing debt you incurred getting there. It is a machine designed to see as many patients as possible, and you are merely a cog in it. Your new ideas, your out-of-the-box visions, your suggestions are met with a resounding, "No, that's not how things are done here."

Your job becomes checking boxes, sending emails, updating electronic charts, attending meetings where new ideas are just laughed at or ignored. Quite frankly, it sucks. Here's the worst part: this noble profession you joined to help make people healthier? It's actually keeping people sick. And the funny thing is, they are as frustrated with the inflexible rules as you are.

That's the problem, these rules—these checklists—they shackle you to the status quo, they stifle your creativity and ingenuity, and they don't prepare you for the unexpected things that patients throw at you. No amount of biochemistry can prepare you for a patient coming to a pharmacy counter, taking off their shirt, and showing you this "rash that's really getting out of hand." There's not a standard operating procedure for when during a phone call to discuss diabetes, a patient literally has UPS deliver his opioid prescription, opens it mid phone call, and realizes his dose has been reduced but that nobody informed him. Good luck finding the algorithm for when, during a blood pressure appointment, a patient insists you refer to his erectile dysfunction as his "boner problem." All of these happened to me, by the way.

The key to finding your own happiness and success within the healthcare system is building the skills necessary to respond compassionately and empathetically to the challenges in healthcare. And if you can do that while maintaining a sense of humor, even better. This book can help teach you how to do that, as well as how to create a more rewarding healthcare experience for everyone, by applying a philosophy I have been studying, practicing, and implementing since 2013: Improv Comedy.

Overcoming Self-Doubt

I was not always the confident, handsome, intelligent, hilarious improv comedy expert pharmacist writing to you today. I only became a pharmacist in 2011, after all.

In fact, I was a hopelessly left-brained pharmacist who found himself struggling to adapt to the unscripted (pun intended) world of pharmacy and healthcare. No matter how many drug interactions, guideline recommendations, or counseling points I could recite from memory, the unexpected patient questions, doctor inquiries, and anything that didn't "follow the script" (pun also intended) of my pharmacy education caused me to struggle to find the right words and actions in the moment.

On paper, I had checked all the boxes that said I was supposed to be a competent, intelligent, and effective pharmacist: a nearly perfect academic record, a pharmacy practice residency at a highly competitive program, and a board certification. Yet when the time came to practice independently outside the sheltered world of academics and multiple-choice tests, I was faced with what seemed like an unanswerable question: What was I supposed to do when a patient or provider went off script? (Pun continues to be intended. In fact, go ahead and assume that every use of the word "script" is a pun in this book; it's a pretty safe bet.)

All of the pharmacy school classes, hours of in-person experiential training, and fancy letters after my name didn't prepare me to create meaningful connections in the moment with those I worked with and cared for, to adapt and remain flexible to uncertain work demands, or to effectively communicate all of my hard-earned knowledge to a diverse patient population. I was struggling to adapt and reach my patients, and questioning my ability as a pharmacist. I lacked confidence that I would ever be qualified to provide the kind of care my patients deserved.

Not only was I struggling to connect on an individual level with patients, but I was also coming to realize all of my training and fancy credentials did not matter much if I wasn't able to effectively adapt, communicate, and problem solve as a member of the healthcare team.

Do you believe a nurse on the floor missing their patient's medication would let it slide because I got really good grades in pharmacy school? Would a patient find comfort in the fact I had passed a test that said I was a "Board Certified Pharmacotherapy Specialist" when they told me they couldn't afford their medications? Would a doctor give me a pass when I couldn't give a clear answer on their crashing ICU patient because I aced my licensing exam?

The answer to these questions, of course, is no. Pharmacists and other healthcare providers focus so much on these outcomes like test scores and GPA, yet according to an article in the *Journal of the American College of Clinical Pharmacy*, objective measures such as GPA could actually screen out qualified pharmacy residency candidates who demonstrate skills in the areas I felt I was lacking.[3]

That is not to say that hard skills aren't important. They are absolutely necessary. My point is that despite traditional training, healthcare providers are still lacking many soft skills needed to be successful. Improv changed everything for me. It helped me apply my hard-earned knowledge and adapt to the infinite challenges inherent in healthcare. Improv helped improve the hard outcomes for my patients, while also helping to create more joy by strengthening our patient-pharmacist relationship.

So what was it specifically that changed for me? How was I able to find the right actions and words in the moment?

---

3. Mate M. Soric, Jennifer D. Robinson, and Timothy R. Ulbrich, "Grade point average is an inappropriate measure of a residency candidate's knowledge and skills," *Journal of the American College of Clinical Pharmacy* 2, no. 2 (24 January 2019): 177–180, https://doi.org/10.1002/jac5.1076.

How did I finally find the joy and satisfaction of providing that care I knew my patients deserved?

Two simple words would change everything for me: "Yes" and "And."

I learned these foundational words in my first improv class back in 2013. These two words unexpectedly launched me on a quest to show how applying basic improv skills could improve the whole healthcare experience.

Improv: More Useful than the Krebs Cycle

Pardon me as I give a bit more of my backstory to set the stage as to the how and why improv has made such an impact on my own life, and how I think it will help transform yours as well.

One of the most common questions I get from other pharmacists, doctors, and numerous other healthcare providers is, "How did a *pharmacist* get into improv comedy?" At first blush, this is a sad indictment of pharmacists and our perceived (or actual) lack of a sense of humor. At further blush, it is a sad indictment of the expectations of healthcare providers that I've noticed to be true: we're supposed to be robotic, objective, and humorless, all in the name of "professionalism." As if one could not have a sense of humor *and* be professional at the same time. Pharmacist Alex Barker, in his book *Indispensible*, laments that "professionalism has beaten personality out of pharmacy."[4] This could not be more true.

How did I, the product of a cold and humorless profession, find my way into improv comedy? Well, I always loved *watching* comedy growing up. *The Simpsons, King of the Hill, Saturday Night Live, Kids in the Hall, Seinfeld*—my favorite shows to quote at school to get laughs. I loved getting laughs . . . but I was also practical. When Mrs. Christman, my eleventh-grade chemistry teacher, destroyed my "plan A career" (pitcher for the Chicago Cubs), she recommended being a pharmacist. The left-brained, practical teen that I was researched the topic and I decided at seventeen that I would be a pharmacist.

Practical? Pharmacists were in demand. I knew earning a living was an important part of being an adult. Pharmacists earned a good living. I had a family friend who was a pharmacist, and he never appeared to be crushingly depressed. Seemed like a no-brainer. Oh, that love of comedy? Comedy was what theater kids and people without direction and a "solid life plan" did. I knew that pharmacy was a safe bet. However, as I will explore later in this book, avoiding risks and going the "safe route" is not always the best option in the long run.

Alas, I committed to pharmacy, and I worked my ass off in college. I still watched my favorite comedies and tried to get girls to like me by trying to be funny. During my undergrad, the notion that I could actually do improv myself became a reality when some friends and I went to an improv show put

4. Alex Barker, *Indispensable: The prescription for a fulfilling pharmacy career* (United States: Life Alchemy LLC, 27 February 2019).

10

on by a group of students. Holy cow! There it was—improv! With other people I was in school with! How cool!

Naturally, I never went to another show and otherwise convinced myself that trying out would get in the way of my march to being a pharmacist. No time for improvisation; that Krebs cycle wasn't going to memorize and forget itself. I am not here to shit on biochemistry, but my guess is by the end of this book, I will have convinced you that the utility of improvisation in your day-to-day life dwarfs that of the intricacies of the Krebs cycle.

Alas, comedy again took a backseat to "practicality." In fairness, a lot of things took a back seat to practicality. I *did* get very close with our school library though. Hurray? It wasn't until my last year of pharmacy school at a leadership event that my intrigue for improv was rekindled. The keynote speaker that day had a message that was very improv heavy. In fact, he got some of the audience to participate in a few improv exercises. I was fortunate enough to participate, and it was a huge success. I had fun, I stayed in the moment, and for that time, I remembered that improv was something I had wanted to try.

Of course, I finally took my leap a mere two years later . . .

I had completed my pharmacy residency and gotten a board certification. Life was supposed to be great. Unfortunately, as I alluded to earlier, I was still struggling with the human side of health care. My struggles occurred both on a micro level with individual challenges in my patient interactions and a macro level with my frustration with the healthcare system. At that point, I was only a year and a half into my career—and I was wondering how I was going to make it for thirty-five more years.

Fortunately, my then-girlfriend-now-wife had a birthday gift for me and, recalling my past flirtation with comedy, asked if I wanted improv classes or guitar lessons. Based on the obnoxious strumming and singing that sometimes emanates from my office and the fact that this book is not about guitar playing being an effective tool for healthcare, you can guess which one I chose.

That first day in improv class, I learned those two magical words: *Yes* and *And*. I was never again the same. It also happened to be held in a massage parlor/yoga studio. The biggest moments can have the humblest beginnings. Like so many others in healthcare, I inhabited the world of "no" forty-plus hours a week, but for those two and a half hours every week at improv, I got to hear and say yes . . . that was The Rule. It was refreshing, it was energizing, and yes, it was sometimes scary.

"Yes" means you must agree to whatever is suggested, which can be a little scary if it's unfamiliar territory. If the suggestion was two astronauts on the moon, then you were two astronauts on the moon, even if you never even got to go to space camp. If my scene partner started digging a ditch, I would start digging, even if my dad never let me . . . oh, well, I suppose years of parent-imposed yard work prepared me for *some* of my improv career.

We don't get to hear "yes" much in healthcare. Our default is "no."

"No, we can't approve that medication."

"No, we can't give you more time with patients."

"No, you are in a different discipline. How could you possibly have a good idea?"

Improv philosophy is the opposite of healthcare philosophy. Improv forces us at last to say yes to an idea. Healthcare's default is to stifle them.

Oh, but don't let me forget about "and." "And" means we add something to it: details, emotions, or consequences. Improv is building something together in the moment. Does our experience in healthcare really feel like we are building something? Or is it constantly fighting?

But improv taught me much more than those two very important words. In fact, there were several words that I learned and applied: listening, communication, mindfulness, teamwork, resilience, and flexibility. This book will cover all these topics and share how these improv principles can change healthcare.

These are all skills required for innovation, collaboration, and the success of any team working toward a goal. Improv is a team sport, and it teaches you to be the ultimate team player by setting aside your ego, preconceived notions, and doubts to be open to new ideas, to different opinions, and ultimately solutions.

I took my first class and was enthralled by these seemingly magical yet wildly practical words. Then I took another class, and another, and since that first massage parlor class in 2013, I have had the pleasure of teaching, coaching, and performing improv for thousands of people.

Now, don't get me wrong, playing on stage with your friends is wonderful fun, and I have had countless hours of laughs, fun stories, and friends for life. But something else happened as I immersed myself in the culture of improv.

I applied these magical lessons at work. I became more pharmacist/human and less pharmacist/robot, which sounds like the most boring straight-to-video sci-fi movie ever. I applied them at home with my loved ones and with strangers at the store who didn't realize they were in an improv scene. I became a better team player, and I was finding solutions to problems that previously would stop me. When you really put the tools of improv into practice, it forces you to listen better in your personal relationships. In improv, you can't be thinking about your next line while someone is speaking to you. How often do you find yourself doing that to your patients? How often does this happen when you are trying to bring up a new idea? Improv forces us to stay in the moment.

After a while, I realized improv wasn't just a hobby. Improv wasn't just a "hack" to be better at my job. Although—it *was* a pretty good job hack and, as I will argue in this book, an excellent application for making healthcare better. Improv became a life philosophy I lean on and turn to every single day. It helped me put my ego aside and realize that life is a team sport, and we must lean on each other for success. Improv helped me apply this because improv is the ultimate team sport; you cannot go out there and do it all on your own. It's like an alley-oop in basketball—sure the guy that slams it home gets a roar from the crowd, but he never gets there without the selfless act of someone else passing the ball. As a weekend warrior on the court, I definitely identify with one half of that analogy too.

So that's my pharmacist-turned-improviser story. It has made me a better pharmacist. It has made me a better person. I know that it can make the healthcare experience better for you and your patients.

Improv: Healthcare's Prescription for Finding Humanity

Alright, so I've shared my story, about how improv turned things around for me healthcare-wise, and a little as to why I think improv is the greatest thing since sliced bread. (Full disclosure: I don't eat carbs, and I think any form of bread—sliced, rolls, or loaves—is pure poison.) However, let me prime the pump as to why healthcare definitely needs a STAT infusion of improv.

Healthcare sucks.

"Cory, THANK YOU! I had no idea why I dreaded getting up in the morning. My back hurts constantly, and I don't know my kids names. YES, that's it. Healthcare sucks!"—every MD, PharmD, NP, PA, DO, DDS, RN et al reading that line . . . probably.

Okay, kidding aside.

Healthcare sucks.

It sucks for our patients, who are forced to navigate through an expensive, complex, uncaring bureaucratic system that provides, at least here in the good ol' US of A, very poor value for the money spent. Their healthcare is confusing. It's wasteful. Also, if you look around, it doesn't seem to be doing a very good job at making/keeping people healthy in any way. For real, only 12 percent of American adults are metabolically healthy.[5]

Does it suck for those of us who provide healthcare? Yes! We are forced to navigate through an expensive, complex, uncaring bureaucratic system that provides, at least here in the good ol' US of A, very poor value for the money spent. Their healthcare is confusing. It's wasteful. Also, if you look around, it doesn't seem to be doing a very good job at making/keeping people healthy in any way.[6]

Can you tell I like repetition? I think you can tell I like repetition.

Joking aside, healthcare providers are burning out, are suffering moral injury when we are unable to uphold the level of care we believe in because of our healthcare environment and culture, and aren't actually making a dent in the woeful health of our patients. This isn't the game we signed up for. We wanted to be healers. To be pillars of our community that people trusted with their lives. We wanted to be respected, like those doctors on TV. (I racked my brain trying to think of a cool pharmacist who has been on TV or the movies . . . we are not well represented in the media.)

Who's to blame? How do we fix the mess that healthcare has become?

5. Joana Araújo, Jianwen Cai, and June Stevens, "Prevalence of Optimal Metabolic Health in American Adults: National Health and Nutrition Examination Survey 2009-2016," *Metabolic Syndrome Related Disorders* 17, no. 1 (8 February 2019): 46–52, https://doi.org/10.1089/met.2018.0105.
6. For real, only 12 percent of American adults are metabolically healthy. Seriously, did you read that last footnote?

Those are in different books written by different people, and I don't pretend to have those answers.

However, I think this book can teach us how to make a difference within the system we currently have. We can learn to enjoy providing care while taking back some of our sanity, and in doing so, actually create some of those innovations and changes healthcare so sorely needs.

The Patient Experience: A Teaser

While I will get into the benefits of applying improv philosophy on a macro level in healthcare, I wanted to end this chapter by teasing some of the important pieces of a patient experience and how improv skills may be the perfect tool to improve them.

As I mentioned, it certainly feels like we can't fix or change our healthcare system, although my hope is this book is a small step toward improving it. One of the most frustrating parts is how it dehumanizes both the providers and consumers. It reduces patients to prescription numbers, DOBs, and claim numbers, while the providers are simply cogs in a moneymaking machine for those that never lay a hand on a patient.

We can improve our experience by creating meaningful connections, showing empathy, and creating provider-patient relationships. An article in JAMA discussed five "Practices to Foster Physician Presence and Connection with Patients in the Clinical Encounter."[7] For our purposes, let's replace "physician" with any healthcare provider—although I love my physicians, and we really can't replace you.

1. Prepare with intention.
2. Listen intently and completely.
3. Agree on what matters most.
4. Connect with the patient's story.
5. Explore emotional cues.

How do we teach our healthcare providers to practice these skills? Is there a board certification in connectedness available? Is there a good source of CME that you've heard of that helps you "agree on what matters most"?

This is our problem as healthcare providers: getting all of that knowledge out of our brain and to the patient in a meaningful way so they care, listen, and implement our advice.

I hope to convince you that improv is the perfect tool to humanize healthcare practices and push innovation to new heights. This creates rewarding experiences for both providers and patients.

---

7. Donna M. Zulman et al, "Practices to Foster Physician Presence and Connection With Patients in the Clinical Encounter," *Journal of the American Medical Association* 323, no. 1 (2020):70–81, doi:10.1001/jama.2019.19003.

Chapter 2

YES, AND

*Two Words You Need to Know
(And May Get Tired of Hearing)*

See the World through an Improv Filter

This book is not intended to be a "how to" improv manual. For that, I recommend *The Upright Citizens Brigades Improvisation Manual*[8] and *Truth in Comedy*.[9] Those two books will get into all of the technicalities of improv comedy. For our purposes, a broad overview of what improv entails will suffice to give us what we need to make our lives and our patients' lives better.

The main rule of improv is to say "yes, and" or apply that sentiment to whatever is said to you. For example, if an improviser started a scene by saying "We're on the moon,"

8. Matt Besser, Ian Roberts, and Matt Walsh, *The Upright Citizens Brigade Comedy Improvisation Manual* (Comedy Council of Nicea, LLC, 2013).
9. Charna Halpern, Del Close, and Kim Johnson, *Truth in Comedy: The Manual for Improvisation* (Pioneer Drama Service, June 1994).

and their partner in the scene replied, "No we're not, we're in a bounce house," then the entire premise of that scene would be negated. The two improvisers would then have to spend time justifying why that first person thought they were on the moon, instead of building upon that scene with interesting details, emotions, and consequences.

After one of my long, convoluted attempts to describe improv to one of my in-laws, he took away that improv was the ability to agree in order to "build something together in the moment." Couldn't have said it better myself. In fact, I didn't. If you disagree or say no in an improv scene, then everything stops. But when you choose to agree, the world of possibilities opens up and anything can be possible in a scene.

Now, how does a place where the rule is to say "yes" to whatever is said sound compared to the resolute world of "no" we inhabit in healthcare? How does it compare to your everyday life? If you are like me, I hope you see how much happier, productive, and innovative that world is where the default answer is "yes."

Improv, I learned, is more than simply saying "yes, and" on stage. It is a code to live by and a philosophy to lean on. Once I began taking my improv attitude from the stage to my life and into healthcare, I became happier by applying what I like to call the "improv filter." It boils down to being able to say yes when our default answer would be no. Of course, in pharmacy, if I literally said yes to everything a patient asked of me, I would not be a licensed pharmacist for much longer. There would probably be a list of patients who would have been harmed because I gave them exactly what they asked for without regards to safety. I am not advocating this! (Although I am excited for my first review that says, "Improv pharmacist says to dispense whatever, whenever, to whoever. SHAME!") What I'm actually saying is that when we apply the "yes, and" filter, we are willing to say yes to the *idea* of something and then building upon it.

Here's an example from the world of Prior Authorizations (which means, for those not in the pharmacy game, the process for getting advanced approval from a healthcare plan before the medication is covered and provided to the patients. Our healthcare system really is the best, ain't it?), where minute details, ridiculous criteria, and obsessive documentation are the norm. My patient had transferred to our system on a non-formulary NSAID. It was so restricted, I had hardly seen it submitted for a prior authorization and even less commonly approved. In the past, my default answer would have been to just tell the patient and their doctor that we probably couldn't approve this; it is highly restricted, so just try an alternative. I'm not saying this would have been great patient care, but I am being honest as to how I would have approached it. I'm arguing that great patient care hasn't been the default mode! However, my "yes, and" filter had been activated. So, I took a deeper dive into that patient's medication history, and wouldn't you know—they met the criteria! The patient and the doctor, whom I had earned extra trust points with, were incredibly grateful.

Now, I would like to clarify that this was a situation where I did not just literally say "yes" to a request, but I applied the "yes, and" filter. A literal "yes" would have just meant approving the medication without the required investigation into its appropriateness. This quick, literal "yes" could have led to outcomes just as bad as our often default attitude of saying no. Instead, I took the spirit of "yes, and" to be to agree to the idea that this med could be appropriate despite its rare approval, as opposed to just saying no. I then "anded" it by doing a thorough review that in fact showed it was a "go" to approve. Ultimately, the patient and provider were satisfied, and all it took was applying the spirit of "yes, and."

Now, this example is all well and good, but what about patients who are, put politely, less grateful for the care they receive? How would applying the improv filter work with them? By being willing to listen and agree to their frustration, we can find common ground toward their care.

Another example: I was referred a patient for diabetes management, but in our first phone call, he was wary of my intent, and essentially all the care he had already received. The reason: nobody would listen to him when he complained that he couldn't sleep, and he thought his metformin was causing it. Insomnia is not listed as a common side effect, and although he had been on the medication for almost a decade, he was insistent it was the cause of his sleep problems. Beyond that, his A1c was uncontrolled, he wasn't checking his blood sugar regularly, and he was not engaged in his care.

Being presented with this, I "yes, anded" his perspective. I said that yes, it must be frustrating that no one will listen, *and* despite the fact that metformin is not a common cause of insomnia, let's take a break for a couple weeks and see what happens. I advised him that he would need to check his blood sugar regularly to see what impact, if any, holding his metformin would have, and that I'd call back in a couple weeks.

The next time I heard from him was two days later. He was calling concerned that his blood sugar was elevated. I considered this a win. How was this a "win" if his sugar was not controlled? Because I had got him engaged in his care. I had been willing to agree to his point of view and concern, and built trust in that moment when others had failed him over a decade. It would have been easy to dismiss such an uncommon, and quite honestly, unlikely medication side effect. However, I was able to address it with the one-two punch of "yes, and." First, I simply agreed to his idea that his metformin may have been the source of his insomnia. Simply getting away from the reflexive "no" is a huge step in the right direction. Yet, if I simply only agreed, without adding to the plan and relationship I was building, we would not have been able to make progress on his engagement in his care. Not only did I agree, I also added a detailed plan that the patient was also able to say "yes, and" to by agreeing to the plan and then following through. This collaboration highlights the "building something together" aspect of the "yes, and" filter that can be accomplished by making sure we add once there is an agreement.

These are just two examples of how applying my "yes, and" filter in healthcare improved the experiences and outcomes for both my patients and myself. As you read this book and think about ways to apply the "yes, and" filter, remember to shift your default response to a "yes" to the idea, concern, or problem of the patient in front of you. Tell yourself to try it for a day, then a week, and see if you and your patients notice a difference. My guess is you will find that despite the obvious limitations put on us by the systems we may work in, you and your patients will be happier with both the interactions and the outcomes.

However, in the bigger picture of healthcare, our default answer is generally "no." Think about it. What is the usual response you get from your supervisor, manager, or administration when you come up with a new idea for your practice site? This could be a shift in schedule, trying to telework, a new program for managing a portion of your patient population, or any number of innovations. The default response, if you're lucky, is "I'm sorry, no." The kindest "no's" always have an apology first. How kind before crushing your idea! On an interdisciplinary team, how often does the advice of the "lower status" member get listened to and incorporated? Later in this book, I will discuss team dynamics and energy sharing, but for now, understand that by ignoring the expertise of someone with a "lesser degree" we may be missing a huge problem that ultimately harms the patient. It's easy to say yes when we can put our ego aside.

So why the default answer of "no"? No is safe. Healthcare, with good reason, promotes a culture of safety, and by default gets stuck in this "no" mindset. Those who live life with a "no" mindset never take risks, never get outside their comfort zone, and thus will never be rewarded by the new ideas, experiences, and adventures they have when saying yes. Anything new or innovative, or God forbid, not the standard of care, is often denied or laughed away. Am I advocating for the reckless practice of medicine? No. Unfortunately, by defaulting to no, our healthcare system, and our practice environments, will remain stagnant, frustrating, and ripe for employee burnout.

There is good news though! We can train ourselves out of our "safety" zone of no. For me, it was training to think like an improviser. For you, maybe it means the same thing, you take improv classes, catch the fever—for which the only cure is more improv—and realize the power of "yes, and." For those less inclined to take a class, simply taking my advice above and applying it to your practice will help you reap the benefits of an improv filter. If you are reading this and have some power in healthcare administration, it means it's time to at least *agree to listen* and then actually *consider* the concerns, ideas, and suggestions brought forth by your staff.

As an example, I had wanted to telework for four years. Every year at my annual review, I asked, usually sheepishly, about the chance to work from home, for at least some of the time. My supervisor, to her credit, never outright said "no." She would *listen* to my reasons, address my concerns, and agreed to see about making it a possibility when "the time was right." It gave me some hope I could someday work from home, and I appreciated her honesty and willingness to consider this "outside the box" idea. Lo and behold, four years after my initial sheepish request, the time was right, and I got to start my telework career. In that time, I could have chosen to leave my facility, change position, or sulk about not getting my way. However, my supervisor, even though she couldn't get me what I wanted at the time, agreed to my idea and was able to make it a reality when the appropriate time came along.

Whether you are a front line employee or in a position of management, putting a "yes, and" filter to your responsibilities opens more doors and opportunities for innovation, new ideas, and ultimately a happier existence in healthcare. Let me also suggest: don't hang up your "yes, and" on the way out of the door at the end of the day. My life, and yours, will be filled with many more opportunities, experiences, and positive relationships if you are willing to apply them to your life beyond your job.

Don't "Yes, But" It

Before we go any further, I want to make you aware of an imposter that threatens to undo all the goodness that improv filter and mindset can bring. It's worse than a wolf in sheep's clothing. It's worse than a Trojan horse. It's a half-assed "yes, and." It's a but! Not to be confused with a whole ass, which would just be a "butt."

The phrase I am referring to is, "yes, but." This attitude is a fake, an imposter, and it pretends to be your improv friend. When we say yes, we are agreeing to an idea, a premise, or a situation. We then add "and" to build upon it. However, when we follow "yes" with "but" we are essentially saying "no" to whatever has been put before us.

Remember, that the goal of the improv mindset is to connect, collaborate, build, and be open to what's new and different. Say "yes" to the outside-the-box idea or to an odd patient complaint. At the very least, it can help generate discussion, grow confidence in the person who brings that suggestion forth, and promote creativity to solve problems. However, "yes, but" does the exact opposite of that, and often in a condescending way.

My boss, if you recall, did not let me telework right away, but she never "yes, butted" me. It would always be an agreement to my idea, a concern as to why I wanted it, and a promise to try and make it a reality. A "yes, but" response would have gone something like: "Yes, that sounds great, and you'd really enjoy it, but you *know* nobody has done that, and upper management wouldn't like it, and that's before we even talk about how it would affect your workflow."

I was taking care of a patient who had been "yes, butted" quite a bit. There was an illusion of caring happening, *but* nothing was really being done to improve their situation. For a little background, this patient had severe breathing problems. This particular patient also had suffered a Traumatic Brain Injury (TBI) which had left them in a very anxious state as their baseline. Part of their anxiety was about their ability to breathe well. Breathing, as it turns out, is an important part of living, and when it is restricted, it can cause anxiety: especially in those prone to both anxiety and breathing problems.

Because of their underlying conditions, they tended to use a lot of albuterol inhaler and were often requesting early refills of said inhaler. When the refills did not arrive on time for their needs, since our system defaulted to not allow early fills, they would call our clinic requesting assistance. Their first "yes, but" came from the medical assistant who generally took their call. They would listen to the patient and agree that they needed more help; however, they would then add, "but, there's nothing I can do."

The patient was left still anxious and still low on their inhaler. Next, the patient would call our pharmacy that managed the fills and shipping of medications and explain their need of an early fill. The staff there, again, would provide a nice "yes" to agree that it sounded like they would need an early fill to meet their need, *but* rules are rules and an early fill just could not be possible.

This situation was turning into a big ol' bag of buts.

Finally, the patient's complaint was escalated to me, the clinical pharmacist, who heard the patient's plight. I made sure to go into "yes, and" mode and avoid any buts. I agreed that it sounded like they were in need of more inhalers, *and* that I would work with their doctor to find a solution. Which is exactly what I was able to do. As a team, the provider and I discussed the situation, the problems the patient faced (TBI causing anxiety), and that for this patient in particular, they would provide a larger quantity of inhalers with each refill so the patient would not run out. The patient's problem was solved by switching from the imposter helper, "yes, but," to the true hero, "yes, and."

"Yes, but" pretends to care. It pretends to have your back. It pretends that it is all in on your idea or solution. Instead, just when you think you have a case, it stabs you in the back with its ugly, "culture of no" truth.

"Yes, but" *searches* for excuses to say no, to deny, to keep the same shitty status quo. Whereas "yes, and" is a heat-seeking missile of energy, solutions, teamwork, and problem solving. It is all in on fixing the problem, generating a unique solution, and accepting the reality we have and making it even better!

As we move forth in this book, and you move forth in your life to try and apply the improv filter, beware of that big, ugly "but." Keep "yes, anding," and the world of possibilities shall remain open.

Turn Your Problems into Gifts

A woman, probably in her mid-fifties, was very excited to come on stage for our improv jam, a show where any member of the audience could come on stage and play with the official improvisers in our company. This was excellent; having the right energy in improv is a big part of the equation, and it's always easier to coax fun out of an enthusiastic person than a shy person. At this time, I was only a few months into my improv career, but I had been gaining confidence.

I can't recall the specific suggestion from the audience, but our volunteer was energized, engaged, and ready to participate. Then all of us on stage realized something.

She spoke no English.

I can't tell you which Scandinavian country she hailed from, or why she was visiting Tucson in July, in an improv theater with no AC, or why she had volunteered herself to come on stage. Regardless, when we started that scene, she began yelling and moving her body in a way that said, "I don't care if I traveled around the world to a sweaty theater in Tucson, I am going for it." All of us improvisers on stage froze and looked at each other with the, "Oh shit, what the hell do we do with this?" look.

Then Mishell took over. She had been improvising for years and had been coaching several of us. She showed no signs of "oh shit." In fact, she had a "hell yeah" look as she stepped on stage.

She looked at our excitable foreign volunteer, looked at us, and said "Y'all, we got the best hype man on the PLANET here today!" We all smiled, and joined in the energetic scene on stage as our "hype man" kept yelling and dancing to support our scene of hip hop artists who were miraculously communicating, interacting, and having a blast with this "hype man" who spoke no English and had no idea of what the scene was actually about.

What happened here? We took a potential problem—that this person has never done improv, doesn't speak English, and probably doesn't understand *what* is going on at all—to be a gift. This person is now the center of attention in a scene and is making people laugh. The more she goes into her "noise and dancing," the *stronger* that scene can become.

Being able to shift the mindset from what could be conceived as a problem into an actual gift is difficult. However, improvisation teaches us that if we are able to "yes, and" the reality in front of us, we can see whatever happens as a gift. A "problem" patient teaches us a new way to communicate or grow our patience. An "unfair policy" gives us the chance to innovate and adapt. Even as a veteran improviser and pharmacist, I am not perfect at this 100 percent of the time. However, seeing problems as gifts *more* of the time has been instrumental in transforming my former frustrated relationship with healthcare.

In our stage jam experience, Mishell was able to put the stranger on stage in her best light and make the others look good. Applying improv created a great scene from a potential problem. We'll talk more later about the place of ego in improv but improv teaches us that success means making others look good. Had Mishell focused on herself and how she looked in that scene, she likely would have been stuck thinking, "Damn, what I am going to do? She has no clue. This scene sucks, and the audience is going to think we're no good. I wish she'd go back to Scandinavia so I can be funny." I'm not saying this is what I was thinking, but I also can't profess to have thought in the moment that this problem was actually a gift to push the scene forward. Mishell was able to improvise a fun, engaging, and memorable scene by putting the success of others first and seeing what a gift she was given.

When presented with "problems" in healthcare, our knee-jerk reaction is to get frustrated, overwhelmed, and burnt out. However, if we can see challenges and problems as gifts, we will have the satisfaction of innovating and creating the solutions that will provide better outcomes for our patients. For example, this book has been written during the COVID-19 pandemic, which I don't think anyone would argue is anywhere close to a blessing. It is and has been a massive global catastrophe on a number of levels. *However*, despite this immense suffering endured by so many, there have been some "gifts" to come out of it.

First, the rapid pace of new vaccine technology that has not only helped with our current pandemic but also promises to be a weapon against future infectious diseases. Without the urgency to develop and test this new technology against the rapidly evolving viral threat, who knows how long these new solutions would have taken?

Beyond vaccine technology, the workflow of healthcare is likely to change for good as the development and application of telehealth services have been forced to grow and adapt. The forced application of this technology means that more patients can be reached in a more efficient manner for all involved. The concept of commuting has changed, as work-from-home had to become the default for many industries. Working from home has had numerous benefits, from saving time commuting to getting more time with family and reducing the amount of cars on the road (the benefits of which are probably the subject for another book by someone more versed in the implications of lowering our vehicular carbon footprint).

I have had patients whose COVID side effect was a reduction in smell and taste. While they would have preferred not to have had these issues, the "side effect" was a reduction in their appetite, weight, and blood sugar for their diabetes! There are likely other benefits we don't even know about yet, and all from something that objectively most would have liked to have never happened. Yet many have turned this pandemic into a gift, which is often the most we can hope for in a sometimes hopeless and often sad healthcare situation.

I'll close this section with a quote from the great Winston Churchill, who certainly saw his share of problems, yet he had a knack for overcoming and even thriving despite the challenges thrown his way:

"Sometimes when Fortune scowls most spitefully, she is preparing her most dazzling gifts."

It was like ol' Winston was a master improviser. When something seems like an insurmountable problem, work on turning it into a "dazzling gift."

Say Yes to Conflict

"Alright, Cory, you've convinced me so far that improv will help create a 'healthcare utopia' where we say 'yes, and' to build great moments with our patients and staff. But, what happens when there is conflict? Huh, Dr. Improv?! We live in the *real* world where patients are grumpy, administrators are gruff, and surgeons are . . ." not going to get a description because I have already offended enough people.

Yes, I agree, conflict will happen. However, one of the beautiful parts about an improv mindset is that "yes, anding" conflict actually helps to resolve it. When I teach improv to students, they often assume that "great comedy" comes from conflict. Homer Simpson vs. Ned Flanders. The Odd Couple. Jim Halpert vs. Dwight Schrute.

However, we actually teach improvisers not to engage in conflict or arguing. Why is that? First, when people come to a comedy show, they have enough conflict and arguing in their regular lives, so coming to see a comedy show and getting more conflict is no fun. Secondly, to make scenes funnier, we "heighten." To heighten means to take things to the next level and increase the absurdity within a scene. A noncomedic example might be me driving a car, and then I'd drive a truck, then I'd drive a monster truck, and then finally I'd "heighten" to flying a rocket ship. When we have an arguing scene, we can only get angrier and argue more. There is a limit to how far we can take this argument heightening and thus a limit to our comedy, if it even exists in such a scene.

Instead, I teach students to turn their "argument" out toward "the man" or a third party. We can have differing points of view, but there is at the very least common ground built around a reality that we have agreed to live in. This ability to agree on common ground in a disagreement is an improv skill that I have utilized well as a pharmacist.

If you are reading this as a healthcare practitioner, you have no doubt gotten into a disagreement with a patient or colleague before. How productive are arguments? Does either party usually get what they want out of the interaction? The answer is usually no.

Instead of arguing, "yes, and" your reality to find common ground and ultimately find a solution.

An example from the world of prior authorizations comes to mind. A patient of mine had been on a shiny new diabetes medication for some time, and he was transferring to our facility. This shiny new med was not on our formulary, and it had to meet a series of criteria for it to be approved. When I called the patient to say we couldn't fill it just yet, he was quite irate. To paraphrase for a PG reading audience, his opinion was that this was "malarkey" and "foolish" to have to jump through so many layers of red tape to get approval for a medication he had been safely using.

My initial, "pharmacist brain" reaction was, "Of course we need more information! This was a new medication and *not* on our formulary! There are rules, procedures, precautions, good sir! How dare you question our process!" Fortunately, my heavily pragmatic improviser brain weighed in, and I "yes, anded" our situation. "Yes, I agree that this is ridiculous! And I don't like having to climb through red tape any more than you do, sir. And if you are frustrated, just know I have to deal with the same cumbersome rules multiple times a day. If I could make it easier, trust me, we both would be a lot happier. However, these are the rules of the game, and the more specific you can be with all of your other medication trials, the sooner we can get this thing approved and put this mess behind us. How does that sound?"

See how I was able to find the common ground? To turn the argument out toward the "man" of bureaucracy instead of against each other?

Being able to "yes, and" doesn't stop at being useful with patients. I am willing to bet that at some point you have had a disagreement with a colleague over a treatment plan. Egos play a big role in healthcare, and this is where being able to put that "yes, and" mindset to work can pay dividends.

For a part of my career, I helped manage our blood thinner clinic (warfarin specifically, for those anticoagulant nerds out there wondering what medication was our go-to for thinnin' that blood). It was high-stress, high-stakes work, as the wrong dose could set a patient on a path to Bleedsville or Clotstown. Part of our clinic duties was managing anticoagulation around surgical procedures. This took the normal day-to-day operations of keeping warfarin in range and cranked the difficulty and risk up significantly when trying to strike the delicate balance of risk of bleed with a surgical procedure and a risk of a clot. To add icing on top of the risk cake was the need to use injectable blood thinners like enoxaparin in certain patients who could not risk being off their warfarin too long before a surgery.

I am not here to pat myself on the back, but our clinic had the management of blood thinners, especially around surgery, down pretty darn well. So much so that *most* of the providers in our facility gladly deferred to us when it came to managing their patients' warfarin around a surgical procedure.

Emphasis on *most*. I got a chance to put my happy ol' "yes, and" filter to work with one provider in particular who didn't always see eye to eye with our clinic, and by proxy, the guidelines we used to safely manage our patients. One of our mutual patients was scheduled for a surgical procedure, and based on their risk factors, would need to "bridge" their warfarin with some enoxaparin shots. No big deal. Except this provider wanted to hold the patient's warfarin for an exceptionally long time, requiring a longer duration of shots, which would be against the most accepted evidence, and a real pain for the patient.

I had talked to the patient who seemed confused about the plan as well, as we had worked with them before to bridge their warfarin. So, I got ahold of the provider to try and work things out. My gut reaction was to say, "No no no, we aren't doing this, Doc. Sorry not sorry." However, I made sure to be cordial, provide background information on who I was and then what the call was all about. I initiated my attempt to adjust the plan by first saying "yes." My initial discussion started along the lines of, "yes, we can agree that given the patient's clot risk, it is appropriate to hold his warfarin before the procedure, and give enoxaparin to avoid a clot."

I made sure we had common ground and were in agreement. The provider was able to see that I was on the same page. I continued, "And I see you want him to hold his warfarin for quite some time while putting him on the shots."

I clarified exactly what he was doing in order to determine his line of thinking and give him a chance to react.

The provider's response, in short, was that he thought his patient was at higher risk of a bleed, and so he wanted to try the longer hold of warfarin. I again, "yes, anded" this thinking by agreeing he was at a high risk, *and* that the holding of warfarin was appropriate. We had built a rapport, were on the same page of thinking, and had developed a mutual trust. Things were going great, but I still needed to make some changes to the plan, which would be easier now since I had "yes, anded" his plan thus far.

The conversation then turned to the guidelines we used to determine anticoagulation around a procedure like this, while acknowledging his concerns about a high risk. I then said that a standard duration to hold warfarin, which was less than they had wanted, had been shown to be sufficient to reduce the risk of bleeding. I made an offer to further explain the kinetics of warfarin and why that duration was appropriate, but I think the risk of boredom was enough to get them to agree to our standard plan. When I informed the patient, they were ecstatic to avoid the extra shots that would have been required. The provider was appreciative of the information, and once again, "yes, and" had helped "bridge" (pun intended) the gap between two providers who disagreed on a plan.

That's what applying the "yes, and" mindset can do. Another important aspect to remember, as we wrap up the utility of improv for conflict, is to remember who we are working for: patients, their health, and those who care about them. Although there are rare exceptions, patients generally don't come to us looking for a fight. It is usually only after dealing with a frustrating, uncaring, confusing, and cumbersome healthcare system that our patients come to us frustrated and on their last shred of patience. We can meet them halfway by agreeing to their frustrating reality and working to build a solution together.

Create a Culture that Embraces "Yes, And"

Solving our society's health problems will require a herculean effort of teamwork as well as other ideas written by likely smarter people in likely better selling books. Still, our culture needs a radical shift if we are going to create and, more importantly, *accept* the innovations that will be needed.

Here's a question we need to take seriously now: Is there such a thing as a bad idea in healthcare?

Be honest. What do you think about that question? I know what a lot of default answers are: "Of course there are *bad* ideas. There are things that are dangerous, expensive, or that have never been done before!"

I expect that kind of thought, but it's that kind of response and mindset that is rooted in limiting beliefs. There are those who believe that the only way to success is to continue within the current paradigm, and if that's not successful, "paradigm harder!" My contention is that there is no such thing as a bad idea. I think there are bad plans. Bad implementations. Bad practices. Bad polices. But, as far as bad ideas, I never want to hear that. When we label something as a bad idea, the innovator of that idea is shut down, and is unlikely to bring forward another idea in the future. We also lose the opportunity to explore whatever that idea might have been, and it could have lead to a revolutionary solution!

Here is a list of perceived "bad ideas" in medicine from the past:

- GERD could not have been caused by an infection.
  - → Sorry, *H. pylori* says otherwise.
- Washing your hands before delivering a baby is heresy.
  - → It only took decades and countless deaths to reverse this.
- Checklists will take the "Art" out of medicine.
  - → In reality, they help in reducing surgical- and hospital-related complications.

Here are past "good ideas" from medicine:

- Cocaine will fix what ails ya!

- After a heart attack, the best thing you can do is rest and not exercise.
- Got pain? Any pain? Have some opioids!

The examples could go on and on, but I hope you are detecting a pattern. Oftentimes our perceived excellent "standard of care" actually turns out to be doing more harm than good. Unfortunately, our culture is such that when a new idea or treatment is proposed, the proposer is often ignored, ridiculed, or at worst, shunned from their field. Let's take for example a man by the name of Ignaz Semmelweis. Not familiar with the name and/or how to pronounce it? Let me fix at least one of those things (they don't even know how to pronounce his name in Hungary).

Dr. Semmelweis was a Hungarian doctor in the 1840s who discovered the basis of germ theory.[10] He discovered mothers died [from puerperal fevers] at higher rates when their babies were delivered by doctors rather than midwives. Being the hard to pronounce scientist/doctor he was, Semmelweis performed a few, likely non-IRB approved, experiments to get to the root of the problem. He finally fell upon the fact that doctors were often performing autopsies prior to delivering babies, likely transmitting infections to the women, leading ultimately to their death. So, he ordered all doctors and their instruments cleaned with chlorine, which he thought would be effective to help reduce smell, while unknowingly using a powerful disinfectant.

10. Rebecca Davis, "The Doctor Who Championed Hand-Washing and Briefly Saved Lives," *Health News from NPR*, 12 January 2015, https://www.npr.org/sections/health-shots/2015/01/12/375663920/the-doctor-who-championed-hand-washing-and-saved-women-s-lives.

The result? Infection rate dropped. Fewer dead people! You would think this would be cause for celebration amongst his colleagues. Well, his contemporaries were definitely not trained in the "yes, and" mindset. In fact, they were upset that this doctor and his new ideas made them look bad. It took years before hand washing became a regular practice, likely leading to a countless amount of needless suffering and death. As for Semmelweis, he was ignored and ridiculed, eventually dying in an insane asylum. Not exactly great motivation for others considering introducing new or different ideas to the world of healthcare.

This opposition to new or different ideas is an antiquated way of handling innovation and new ideas, and unfortunately the ones who suffer the most are our patients, the very ones we got into healthcare to help. While you may think that this example is old and outdated, just try bringing up a different point of view with a group of your medical contemporaries and see how much support or even interest you get. Healthcare loves our status quo, and change, especially dramatic change like hand washing, often takes decades.

This is why the adoption of the improv mindset is so crucial. We are missing out on untold innovation, we are burning out our most passionate and insightful people, and in the end, our patients are suffering. We usually associate improv with comedy, but it's a solution to the sad consequences of our "no" based culture. And that's no laughing matter.

Before we can move forward, healthcare must embrace this improv mindset to work past this "culture of no." We have to get over the idea that there must be "gatekeepers of the ideas." Our default mode is to stay with the status quo, even if the status quo is killing people (see our poor hand-washing physician advocate), killing people (see our past embrace of cocaine), or killing people (opioids, for goodness sake). If we continue to live in a culture of no, then we will continue to kill our patients. Which, interestingly, is the opposite of why I got into this business, and I am guessing that's the same for you.

Where can we start? Well, I am a big proponent of keeping things within our own locus of control, so let's start on the individual patient level. We can retrain our default response to: odd patient questions, odd patient requests, and just odd patients in general. We all get odd patients. Remember the guy who insisted I referred to his erectile dysfunction as his "boner problem"? We were trying to adjust blood pressure medication so that his systolic blood pressure would go down while still allowing for his erection to raise up. I kept saying, "Sir, we want to address your erectile dysfunction." He kept responding, snickering like Kevin Malone from *The Office*, "You mean my *boner problem*. Because that's what I call it, my *boner problem*, and I'd appreciate if you would as well." A default response might be, "That's wildly inappropriate. I didn't spend six years in college and another in residency to refer to a medical condition like I was talking with my friends when we were seventeen years old back in high school!" But, in that moment, this guy needed me to. So, with a little apprehension, I said, "Yes, I'm sorry, we need to get to the bottom of your *boner problem*. It's *hard* to figure out, but I am sure we can *erect* a solution. So let me give it to you *straight*." (I'm sure my parents will be proud to give their son's book to friends with the caveat that *boner problem* appears four times.)

It took saying yes to an "odd" request, but I had the patient on my side, caring about both his . . . um, I just can't type those words again . . . erectile dysfunction and his blood pressure. We don't do that enough with our patients. I understand the importance of professionalism, but sometimes being professional means being able to relate to our patients, even if means bending the barriers of what we would call "truly professional."

How else can we break the culture of no with our patients? I am prepared for the audible groan (as you ironically may be hearing this via the Audible app), but when patients bring in their own research from "Dr. Duck Duck Go" (oh, you thought I was going to say Dr. Google weren't you? I wanted to make sure that this hypothetical patient's internet advice was *extra crazy*) don't be so apt to dismiss them . . . immediately. Is there a chance that they are bringing you rigorously peer-reviewed studies that are part of an update to the guidelines on the condition you are treating them on? There is a non-zero chance that is the case. Is there a better chance it is a product sold to them on one of these?

a) Late night TV
b) Midday talk show
c) Early morning infomercial

Yes, and if you are looking for the correct answer, it's all of the above, by the way.

Just because they are bringing to our attention a possibly crazy treatment or diagnostic test that is not part of the standard of care does not mean the interaction or idea is all for naught. Lest we judge too soon, what percentage of your patients are not engaged in their own care, don't follow any advice you give, and seem resigned to a medically unpleasant fate? If you practice on planet Earth, where I do, that percentage is exceedingly high. So, put on some rose-colored "yes, and" glasses, and be grateful that the patient in front of you is at least taking part in their own care.

When Saying Yes Does Not Literally Mean Saying "Yes"

If you have not yet abandoned me on this concept and moved on, thank you, and let's dive deeper. Remember, "yes, and" does not mean literally saying yes to whatever is asked or said to you, it means being willing to say yes to the idea. When a patient is bringing us their own perspective and information, they are trying to tell us something. They are providing us their "want" or "why." Maybe, as is the case for most of the patients whom I follow for diabetes, they hate taking so many medicines for their blood sugar. So, for example, when they bring in information or a video on a new way of eating that they're excited about, entertain their perspective, even if it's not standard of care. If they are excited about it, entertain their perspective. The notion that there are seven billion people, and counting, on the planet, and a single "standard of care" that would work for every one of us is biologically and genetically insulting. The rigid adherence to a standard of care does not take into account patient preferences, cultural values, and socioeconomic status.

As long as we "do no harm," we should adapt to information that patients bring us. Either the patient can improve their condition *with* the information they brought, or they can find out that it doesn't work. If we don't immediately give them a harsh "no," they walk away trusting a provider who is flexible, can meet them halfway, and truly listens to their concerns. At worst, we can build trust with patients. At "the middle," the information they give us to research can teach us something new. At best, we'll identify new methods and ideas to help treat patients well beyond the one who is sitting in front of us who brought us that "out of the box" idea. Let us not forget the importance of "gift giving" in improv and healthcare. Metaphorically speaking, our patients are often middle-aged Scandinavian women who don't speak our language, and we're frustrated when we don't see what they bring us is a gift—something to be worked with rather than dismissed outright.

The "cure" a patient brings is sometimes not even about the cure. We can find out they don't want medication, another test, or a procedure. It can teach us a lot about who they trust in medicine and how much they care about their own health. Unfortunately, they too often place their trust in what Dr. Oz says, or what their cousin who works in a doctor's office heard.

I can already feel the blood pressures increasing, the pulse rates going up, and my Amazon review going down. "Cory, I'm a trained (doctor, nurse, etc.) who spent years in training, countless hours researching, and untold dollars on my education. Are you telling me that a patient who spent mere seconds, if using Google, 'researching' this complex medical condition should be trusted and listened to on this very complex subject? Harumph! Harumph, and Good Day!"

First, thanks for wishing me a good day! I'll assume it was a compliment! Second, in short, yes. There is a time for ego, don't get me wrong, and you should feel proud about the exceptional education and training you have received. You are no doubt an expert in the hypothetical situation. However, there is one thing you have not studied and become an expert in over the years: the individual sitting in front of you. If we are willing to say "yes, and" to our patients, we are more likely to know what the answer to their problems are, understand their concerns better, and find a better solution together. We are no doubt technically trained better than ever before, a theme I will allude to again and again, but it is our inability to listen, relate, and apply this training on an individual level that leaves our patients behind.

From here, I'll move our focus from what the individual practitioner can do to a brief glimpse into the macro view of the system's failings.

Creating a Culture of Yes in Healthcare

I certainly don't think that the hardworking healthcare provider who is up to their neck in patients, paperwork, and other minutiae is where the blame can totally be placed, but I think we as individuals can address a lot. The culture within the system as a whole has a bias against new ideas that's antithetical to the open-mindedness that improv teaches.

"The way things have been done" is a common symptom of our healthcare system. This book has the "benefit" of being written during the COVID-19 pandemic. There are a lot of unknowns, so adaptation and improvisation is happening in healthcare right now. "It's always been done that way" is no longer an excuse to keep the status quo. A culture of "yes, and" to new ideas is not only important, it's essential. Some regulations, especially in the space of telehealth, are being altered to allow providers to tackle the myriad challenges facing us today. A willingness to remove barriers that were previously in place by seeking out and being open to new ideas and innovation in the face of problems is one way progress can be made when faced with obstacles to overcome.[11]

It's possible, though, that we've gone from "no" to something else entirely that's not quite "yes." It seems that "no culture" is still running in the background, so it's not quite been a 180. Would you believe a 90? How about a 45? Things like state licensing, telemedicine, and novel treatments are

11. The National Telehealth Policy Resource Center, "Fact Sheet: COVID-19 Telehealth Coverage Policies," *Center for Connected Health Policy*, March 2021, https://www.cchpca.org/resources/covid-19-telehealth-coverage-policies/. "CARES Act: AMA COVID-19 pandemic telehealth fact sheet," *AMA*, last updated 27 April 2020, https://www.ama-assn.org/delivering-care/public-health/cares-act-ama-covid -19-pandemic-telehealth-fact-sheet.

advancing light-years faster than before.[12] I can say one group has loved the new approaches like telemedicine: patients.[13] While the progress in telemedicine and other treatments has been heartening with respect to our COVID response, the overall healthcare culture still remains mired in a culture of no that frustrates patients and providers alike.

Remember, those entities we signed up to take care of? Patients love being able to get the care they need from their own home, or car, or tractor, or whatever wind tunnel they wandered into (some of them really sound like that). Think of some of the biggest dissatisfiers when visiting the doctor's office: crowded waiting room full of *sick people*, boring magazines, and a TV that is perpetually on a cooking show where they are preparing food your doctor will tell you to avoid. Now, they get to bypass all of that and just get the sweet, sweet doctor time they wanted in the first place.

Too often, something like telemedicine has been "too complicated," "too risky," and "too hard on patients." *Miraculously,* within a few weeks, the country has almost completely transformed into a telemedicine platform.

"But, it was going to be too hard."

Malarkey.

---

12. Iris Hentze, "COVID-19: Occupational Licensing During Public Emergencies," *NCSL*, 30 October 2020, https://www.ncsl.org/research/labor-and-employment/covid-19-occupational-licensing-in-public-emergencies.aspx.
"Coronavirus (COVID-19) Update: FDA Takes New Actions to Accelerate Development of Novel Prevention, Treatment Options for COVID-19," *FDA*, 11 May 2020, https://www.fda.gov/news-events/press-announcements/coronavirus-covid-19-update-fda-takes-new-actions-accelerate-development-novel-prevention-treatment.
13. Sara Heath, "Telehealth Patient Satisfaction High, Paves Path for Future Access," *Patient Engagement HIT*, 1 July 2020, https://patientengagementhit.com/news/telehealth-patient-satisfaction-high-paves-path-for-future-access.

A rigid, close-minded culture of "no" kept this and other very satisfying innovations stifled. However, when our healthcare system was forced to *improvise*, we have been able to make significant strides that have benefitted both sides of the healthcare equation. The reason? Circumstances forced them to adopt an attitude of "yes, and" and reap the rewards of previously stifled innovation.

On a positive note, it does seem that there is some "yes, and" hiding in our healthcare system. The ability to quickly adapt to a global pandemic by quickly cutting the red tape needed to provide better care to patients via telemedicine is an excellent example. Although I have painted a rather bleak view of our "culture of no" in healthcare, I think there is plenty of agreement to innovation and new ideas hiding beneath the surface. It is not all "no" all the time. There are those of us who want to make changes for the better, who have these new ideas and innovations, and managers and administrators who have the heart and mind to make it happen. Yet there is work to do to overcome the slow-moving status quo, as it still falls short in providing the optimal care for our patients.

Our challenge now is to do some stifling—stifle the culture of no. Squash the "anti new idea" sentiment. Also, don't wait for a doggone pandemic to listen to new ideas. Follow me on this: you can just listen to new ideas *despite* a lack of a global pandemic.

Radical, I know.

Chapter 3

EMPATHY

How Improv Can Help Us
Treat Our Patients Like
Actual Human Beings

Up next, we are going to tackle one of healthcare's many struggles: lack of empathy. Before we dive into how improv can train us to be more empathetic providers for our patients, first a pop quiz:

What is the difference between sympathy and empathy?

Before I give you the answer, I'll ease your mind with this data: My wife, who has gone from critical care RN to NP and in the process earned three degrees, including a masters and a doctorate, who cares for our two sons with love and compassion, and who has earned a blue belt in Brazilian Jiu Jitsu, could not properly differentiate between the two.

With that being disclosed, here it goes:

Empathy can be defined as a person's ability to recognize and share the emotions of another person. It involves the ability to see someone else's situation from their perspective and share their emotions, positive or negative. Sympathy is a feeling of care and concern for someone, often someone close, accompanied by a wish to see them better off or happier.

The big difference is that sympathy, unlike empathy, does not involve a shared perspective or emotion.

Why is empathy important? Because it can help us connect with our patients, show them that we care, and communicate more effectively.

It can be easy after a long day to forget that every patient has a history, family, and motivation for their actions. If we can empathize with what they are feeling in the moment and share in their experience, we can then proceed more effectively in a plan that will be not only helpful for, but also more likely accepted by, our patients.

So we have a nice warm and fuzzy definition of empathy, and I have cemented my place in the doghouse with my wife. The reality is in healthcare that we suck at empathy. We suck at finding a shared perspective with our patients, we suck at finding a shared perspective from our colleagues and managers, and we suck at finding a shared perspective between those doing the managing and administrating and those providers on the front line.

Really, let's think about the healthcare experience from the consumer side for a moment. When was the last time you went to your doctor and left thinking, "Wow, they really *get* me"? Or you went to the pharmacy to drop off your prescription and happily waited an hour for it to be ready? Or perhaps you had an x-ray done on an aching part of your body and afterward you called your friend and said, "That x-ray tech didn't just see inside me, they really saw *inside* me"?

These scenarios seem far-fetched, but does it really have to be this way? Our inability to connect with patients, to see the world through their eyes, and to be able to empathize with them on what is often their worst day is a huge impediment to gaining their trust and ultimately to their listening to our treatment recommendations to improve their health. Of course, from a healthcare provider's perspective, we may be thinking, "It only matters that they get the right treatment and we save their life. What more can these greedy patients ask for?"

To be treated like a human.

A story to hammer home this point. While I was writing this book, my grandfather passed away at the ripe old age of ninety-two, but he should never have made it past fifty-five. In 1984, he was having serious heart trouble, serious enough to merit quadruple bypass surgery. He was one of those who literally "died on the table" during the operation. However, thankfully for me and the rest of our family, Grandpa got a new lease on life. Selfishly, I got to have a grandfather who taught me how to fix things, which I promptly forgot, how to grow peas in the garden, and how to get triple samples at Costco. (He would say, "I need one for me, my wife, and my grandson" while telling me to say to the Costco Sample Overlords, "I need one for me, my grandma, and my grandpa." Let's just say Grandma was not in our little lunch plan.)

Objectively, this operation was a complete success, minus the part where Grandpa got to put in reservations for lunch with St. Peter. However, my dad tells a story that boils my blood to this day. Once the operation was complete, the surgeon and my dad ended up in the elevator. The surgeon, recognizing my father, says, "You're Mr. Jenks's son, right?" My dad confirms his suspicions. The surgeon replies coldly, "Yeah, we sure didn't think he was going to make it. How 'bout that?" and gets off the elevator.

My CT surgeons are reading this thinking, "So, what is the problem here?" However grateful I am for the outcome of the surgery, the surgeon completely lacked empathy for someone who came so close to losing his father. My dad is still pissed about that surgeon to this day. The fact that the memory of the elevator is one of the most enduring of the surgery that saved his dad's life should teach us about the importance of empathy and at the very least, attempting to understand what patients might be going through.

We have identified what empathy is and how much of a gap we have in healthcare, but how can we close it? Well, since you are reading a book about improv, and its subsequent utility in healthcare, lets again work on utilizing the "improv filter." Improvisers are taught that when they create or play a character on stage they should give that character a "want" or a "why." When we can establish a strong want or why, everything that our character says on stage is filtered through that want. Creating that strong want is crucial in creating a scene or character with depth that can respond to whatever happens on stage. Creating a character in the moment with a name, background, history, desires, and strong reactions, and to *think* and know everything about that character would be nearly impossible. However, this task becomes infinitely easier if we know exactly what that character wants. Then, everything they say or do is filtered through that character. Easy comedy. In reality, the comedy is not always easy, or comedic, but it makes things so much easier having that strong point of view.

An example of this "easy comedy" happened in a scene I'll call "first responder Happy Hour." I started the scene with multiple people by saying, "Alright, it's first responder happy hour! Great to see you EMT, policeman, and fire-fighter. It's great to have a place to relax, decompress, and talk shop with other stressful professions like myself, a mall security guard."

This quickly evolved into one of my most memorable scenes as each other representative from a truly dangerous profession would describe a horrific event that drove them to Happy Hour. My character would try to fit in by describing their own "horrors": a dog pooping by the Cinnabon, teenagers loitering, a theft of scented candles from the Bath and Body Works! I had never met this character, but everything I said or did flowed through his desire to be a "dangerous" professional.

It all comes from a want or a why.

Think of yourself in your daily, even non-healthcare part of life. Maybe you want to be loved, or for someone to appreciate all of the hard work you do in the yard. (Honey, I hope you have decided to read your husband's book . . . and that you see this.) Perhaps it is to help people to live happier and healthier lives. Maybe you want to write a book to make the healthcare experience better for all involved by applying improv!

Our patients all have those same wants in their daily life. Most have them related to their healthcare. However, if we are unable to tap into what it is that they really want, to find their "why," then any advice or instructions we give will simply be in vain. It is all about tapping into what the patient cares about in relation to their health.

Here are a few examples of "wants" that I have come across:

- To get off insulin
- To fix their "boner" problem and their blood pressure problem
- To be around for grandkids
- To save money by quitting smoking
- To have someone actually listen to them

These are just some of the underlying healthcare-related "wants" I have encountered. However, the last one is the one that sticks out most for me as being the most effective at being the gateway to getting a patient engaged in their care.

Unfortunately, most patients simply don't feel listened to. As I have gone over in detail, their own ideas and desires are often bulldozed by healthcare providers. There is no sharing of energy and communication is abysmal.

As healthcare providers, if we can develop the ability to identify a patient's "want" or "why" in the few precious minutes we get, I believe we will be able to show better empathy, develop trust, and work better with our patients. Overall, patients will appreciate being heard, and our enjoyment of the entire healthcare experience will improve. However, it is incumbent upon us as the healthcare provider to work hard, listen, and identify what that patient cares about.

If this concept seems abstract, let me provide a hypothetical example:

We're seeing a patient who smokes. They have smoked a long time, and they love lightin' up all times of the day. When inquiring about quitting, they are not interested. We could end right there, and move on . . . or we can put our why and want detective hats on and figure out what this person is feeling, what motivates them, and what *could* help them consider quitting. Their want or why could be anything—saving money, seeing grandkids, or stickin' it to Big Tobacco.

As you can see, finding that want can lead to better health outcomes. Sometimes, though, it's just about having a better interaction outcome. This could mean identifying that a patient truly isn't ready to talk about tobacco cessation, or diabetes, or blood pressure, but that they just want someone to talk to. My nurse-practitioner-who-couldn't-define-empathy wife is a master at this. Full disclosure, she has also taken improv classes and works in pulmonology and, dammit, sometimes patients just want to talk about their anxiety, which in fairness can affect breathing. She can quickly recognize when an appointment is just not going to meet her pre-planned goal, and thus she is able to *improvise, empathize,* and ultimately garner engagement and trust so that the next time she talks to that patient, they will be more likely to trust my wife and her recommendations.

To really help you see the human cost of a lack of empathy, I will turn back to my family. My *other* grandfather was a veteran of World War II. What did he do? Let's just say his "supervisor" was a guy by the name of General George S. Patton, and "Old Blood and Guts" didn't shy away from a fight. Poppa, as I lovingly referred to my grandfather, got to see his fair share of Nazi hostility. One example was being blown out of an open half-track truck when it "found" a German mine. Poppa was blown out of the truck, landing "fortunately" on his head. He was shaken up, but refused any medical treatment. There is a reason his was the "Greatest Generation."

This was in February of 1945. He still had three more months of fighting until he got to come home. Years after he came home, surprise surprise, he developed neck problems. He had trouble straightening his head up. He ached all the time. He could not sit under any sort of air conditioning at a restaurant—although this is a trait quite common, I have found, in our geriatric population.

He served his country and was likely due some sort of compensation for his sacrifice.

Being the greedy old man he was, he finally sought out his compensation . . . sixty years after the event, in his mid-eighties. For years, he was due something from his country he had served, but he had neglected to pursue it. But why? Objectively, he was injured and deserved compensation, a handicap placard for his car, and a "thank you" from his country. Yet he didn't seek any of it until very late in his life. Why was that?

Based on our conversations, there were a number of reasons:

1. He didn't want to be "a bother."
2. He didn't trust the VA.
3. He didn't want to take it from someone who "really needed it."

If you can't tell, my grandfather was quite the selfish asshole. Also, if you can't tell, he passed on his sense of sarcasm to his handsome pharmacist grandson.

He truly was a humble, polite man who had seen others of his peer group who did make a "fuss" about their condition, and he wanted nothing to do with it. He had also had a few run-ins with providers at the VA when treating his PTSD. One said he needed to find Jesus. My grandfather tried to explain that he was Jewish, and that would just not do. Do you detect a lack of empathy?

He also was fairly financially secure, and his wife had required a handicap spot. More than one occasion, Mama, which is how I lovingly referred to my grandmother, did not have a place to park because someone else had taken the handicapped spot. Poppa was afraid of getting in the way of someone like that.

He finally sought compensation after his handsome, sarcastic, future-pharmacist grandson had read about his "little incident with a German land mine" and pressed him for more information. At this point, my grandmother had passed away, and he did not have too much on his hands to keep him busy. So, at the urging of myself and my mother, he went through the process for VA disability and received what he had earned.

For years, my grandfather had suffered in physical and mental pain, but no one caring for him had been able to connect in a way to make him care about what he had earned or the other resources available to him. Once he did try and seek care, his own personal beliefs were completely ignored. That was a significant failure in empathy and ability to connect, thus he became disengaged in the care he had earned.

Now, take his one case and multiply it by the millions who access healthcare. How many patients are disengaged despite the billions we spend? How many patients feel like no one will listen to them? Or care about them?

We can fix this, and it is not complex. By working our "empathy muscles," utilizing the tools of improvisation, and garnering their trust we can better connect and empathize with our patients, help them leave the interaction feeling understood and appreciated, and ultimately lead them on the path to healthy lives. Which is what we got into this business to help them achieve.

Empathize to Build Trust as an Employer

Gaining the trust of our patients while working on the frontlines of healthcare is paramount. However, there is more than the patient-professional interaction. There is the professional-organization relationship. An important measuring stick for this is employee engagement, which is the type of emotional commitment an employee has to its company and goals. It's not just about being a happy employee, it is about caring for the patients . . . and the organization's goals.

So what is the big deal if an employee for a healthcare organization is not engaged? Medical errors increase. In this Gallup poll of over two hundred hospitals, the number one predictor of mortality was the *engagement level of their nurses*.[14]

Another study from across the pond in the NHS in England showed that improving engagement reduced MRSA cases, reduced mortality, and reduced employee turnover.[15]

So it appears employee engagement is not only a big deal, it can be the difference between life and death for our patients. If I were in charge of a large healthcare organization, what would my move be? I would play to my strengths and see how and where improv and employee engagement meet. A solution for engagement provided by improv training is summed up in one word: Empathy.

When employees trust in their organization, they are more likely to be engaged with their job, and a way for the organization to build this trust is by empathizing with those working on the front lines. As I have explained, identifying a

14. Rick Blizzard, "Nurse Engagement Key to Reducing Medical Errors," Gallup, December 27, 2005, https://news.gallup.com/poll/20629/nurse-engagement-key-reducing -medical-errors.aspx

15. Michael A. West and Jeremy F. Dawson, "Employee Engagement and NHS Performance," The King's Fund, 2012, https://www.kingsfund.org.uk/sites/default /files/employee-engagement-nhs-performance-west-dawson-leadership-review2012 -paper.pdf

wish or want is a great way to gain the perspective of another person. As an employer, focusing on at least *some* wants or wishes of your employees would go a long way in garnering their trust and driving their engagement.

A healthcare organization can often ask a lot of its employees that make them less than excited. This could be mandates on patient appointments, expectations for prescription wait times, or any number of well-intentioned "corporate plans" that seem like a great idea in a boardroom but are hell for the frontline staff. As an example, I was a pharmacy intern at a Big Box store. I don't work there anymore, and they don't have their own pharmacy department either, so I can safely say it was Target. Sorry Target. Love your weekly ads, hate your past corporate pharmacy policies.

One of their ideas to "drum up business" was to offer Target gift cards for new and transferred prescriptions. As a pharmacist professional, I roll my eyes a bit at the gift card game, but as a business, I understand the need for more 'scripts through the door. So offering the incentive was not a huge issue for me.

However, they thought it was brilliant to have pharmacists and interns roam the aisles of Target, soliciting business. Think about how you as a patient and/or Target shopper would feel, while in the greeting card aisle picking out sympathy cards when a red-shirted white-coated pharmacists walks up to you to ask about your prescription history:

"Excuse me, it looks like you are in the market for a sympathy card. Feeling a little blue? Are you taking anything for it? If so, think about transferring that antidepressant here, and we'll chip in to help ease the pain of your loss by easing the strain on your wallet."

Most of my interactions went a little something like this:

Me: "Hi there, can I help you find something?"

Target guest: "Yes, I was actually looking for some picture frames"

Me: "Sorry, I work in the pharmacy, it looks like I, in fact, cannot help you."

Me, back in the pharmacy: "Yep, talked to another person, we can't help them, but mark it down!"

Oh yes, this uncomfortable practice came with obligatory tracking that had to be turned in to corporate to show how much we were "engaged" with building the Target business. I can assure you, this well-intentioned plan did *not* build trust or engagement. It did, however, help me learn early on how to "check a box" while doing minimal work for a task that, to put it kindly, was bullshit. I suppose the joke is on Target Pharmacy, because they are now CVS pharmacy. Who would have thought hitting people up in the video game aisle for their prescription history wouldn't work?

I can tell you who: everyone working on the front lines at Target.

I would say that trolling strangers at Target for prescription transfers was probably the dumbest thing I have had to do in healthcare. Really, it's hard to top its stupidity in my career. Who knows how many countless hours were spent roaming the aisles that were taken away from what pharmacists got into this profession to do: take direct care of patients. Yet, if the geniuses up the corporate ladder who thought up this scheme had a shred of empathy, they would probably have known no pharmacist wanted to rub elbows with someone in the pet food aisle while asking if they wanted to transfer their allergy medication (Oh, you think the person in aisle 7 covered in cat hair *doesn't* take anything for allergies?).

Putting themselves in their employees' shoes for a moment would have hopefully kept them from focusing on squeezing every last penny of profit and every last shred of dignity from their pharmacists, and instead on something a little less humiliating and objectively ineffective.

For those leading healthcare organizations:

Want to save lives, save money, and keep your healthcare employees?

Show some empathy and give them a reason to trust you.

Chapter 4

PREPARE FOR THE UNPREDICTABLE

Your Guide to Dominating What You Didn't Even See Coming

Learn to Play by the Rules

Improv has a lot of rules. No, really, the form of theater that is completely made up on the spot, with no scripts, and that is usually started from an audience suggestion has a whole list of 'em. When I explain this fact to my friends and family, they are utterly confused. However, improv without any rules and structure would be 100 percent chaos and would be 100 percent unwatchable and terrible. Here are a few of the rules that we do our best to abide by on stage:

- Say yes and add details, emotions, and consequences.

- Avoid asking questions.
- Don't go for a cheap joke.
- Establish a who, what, and where.
- Be specific.

When we have an improv class or rehearsal, these are some of the things that we work on. Yup, rehearsing improv. However, it is important to hone these specific skills to be successful on stage. I'll use a sports analogy. Let's take my favorite sport, America's pastime. No, not arguing on Facebook comment sections—baseball.

Baseball has a set of rules and certain skills to work on. It requires practice to have any sort of success at it, or if you are me, it takes lots of practice to be barely passable. Within each game, though, while utilizing the framework of skills and rules, anything can happen. In fact, you'd be hard pressed to ever find two baseball games where the exact same thing happened.

Any sport, improv scene, or, as I bring you back to the focus of this book, healthcare encounter has a set of skills, rules, and outcomes. But within each of these, anything can happen. Those who are most prepared skill-wise and who understand the rules the best, generally have more success. (Unless you are the New England Patriots, then the rules need not apply.) In healthcare, we do an outstanding job of teaching the technical skills required to be a doctor, nurse, pharmacist, etc. Unfortunately, where I think we fall short is on the human side of things.

Let's discuss the fact that we have highly trained health-care professionals, well versed in the laws of their jurisdiction, who know how each "game," or patient encounter, should be played. There are guidelines, algorithms, and standards of care that help guide our decisions. What happens when a patient doesn't fit neatly into our guidelines or checklists though? How well do we handle the gray area?

I think we suck at it, personally. We are like healthcare robots that get to a situation that doesn't make sense and say, "Does not compute." We find out the hard way that the patient in front of us is not just a series of zeros and ones, but a real, living, breathing person. Ultimately, the patient suffers because of our inability to communicate and decide, and we suffer from self-doubt and burnout from feeling like we are falling short.

What I'll acknowledge before bashing our healthcare field any more is that structure *is* important! We need our guidelines, we need solid evidence on which to base our decisions, and we need a framework to practice in. This is the case in every field or profession, whether you are a surgeon, a shortstop, or an improv performer. Humans crave structure, but when we become overly reliant upon it, we struggle mightily when something interrupts it. For healthcare, it could mean a non-adherent patient, a person facing a socioeconomic challenge, or a third-party payer that doesn't want to pony up for what you thought was a great therapeutic plan.

Before I learned and embraced the improv mindset, I was short circuiting all the time! Patients who reacted wildly different from what I had planned, patients who had no concern over what we were "supposed" to discuss, and patients who had no desire to even see a pharmacist would put me on my heels, fill me with doubt, and leave me "uh-ing," stuttering, and grasping for anything to take care of what they needed.

But then I became an improviser, where I learned to dance with chaos and it allowed me to prepare for the unpredictable. While we are technically more advanced than ever as healthcare providers, with more resources and data at our fingertips than ever before, we aren't good at preparing for the inevitable unknowns. I believe one of the reasons is that we are never permitted an environment to make mistakes. Of course, I am not advocating for mistakes in patient care. However, if we think of the typical healthcare provider's training, starting from a highly competitive undergraduate environment that compels them to study, to then get into a professional school, and then postgraduate training, there is very little "give." Every test, every presentation, every interview is high stakes. While I don't disagree that it's crucial to prepare healthcare providers for the high stakes environment we will inhabit, it is foolish to ignore the cost of perfectionism in training.

Moreover, when trying to teach the soft skills required to react in an unpredictable environment, we fall short in providing a way for trainees to make mistakes without worrying about the consequences. Improv training is the opposite of that: it's a welcoming, low-stakes environment that embraces risk-taking and helps to build confidence in uncertain situations. It's why improv training has been incorporated into the professional curriculum at the University of Arizona's College of Pharmacy where they have realized the importance of teaching not just the technical but also the human side of healthcare.

So, how do we teach our healthcare providers to prepare for the unpredictable? Well, duh, this book is about applying improv, so, yes, improv is an excellent modality. While we don't need every physician to know how to do an accent, or every nurse to be an expert on improvised rapping (although, who wouldn't want a nurse who could rap the instructions to them?), we can apply the principles of improvisation in some sort of structured role playing or training, both in professional school, and as part of continuing education or facility specific training to help them be more flexible in the face of the unpredictable.[16]

Flex Your Flexibility Muscles

Surprising as it may seem for an improv comedian, I love routine. I may have adopted the mindset and philosophy of an improviser, but deep down in my brain, I am still that Type A, left-brained pharmacist. Pharmacy attracts a, how shall I say this, "certain" kind of person. It attracts the type of people who like rules, structure, and order. It attracts the kind of people who do well in a controlled environment that rewards double-checking and identifying errors. It attracts people that thrive on algorithms, stepwise approaches, and taking an "A to B to C" route of a problem. We show up on time, usually early. We are the type of people who will show

---

16. Here is a link to a fun game for you to practice some improv skills with your team: https://youtu.be/AZWq4jXNL2E

up to the airport two and a half hours early, even when an hour would do, because "you just never know."

Pharmacists love order. Chaos and entropy frighten us.

Having a Type A mindset serves pharmacists and others in healthcare well in many respects. It is important, for the sake of safety, to have individuals and organizations that like to follow rules, regulations, and procedures. As someone who has been Type A for my entire life, and a pharmacist for about a third of said Type A life, this mindset is really useful for getting stuff done. Boy, can we get stuff done when provided with a rigid schedule, plan, and path. I think having a set of boxes to check is what attracts a lot of people to pharmacy, and healthcare in general. As I look back on how I found my career path, it was all very logical, even to a hormone-riddled seventeen-year-old in high school:

- Someday I will need a job, preferably one that is as secure as possible.
- I enjoy math and science.
- Pharmacy utilizes math and science.
- Pharmacists are highly sought out and well-compensated professionals (this was the mid 2000s before a glut of pharmacy schools and an abrupt lack of demand changed this equation, but bear with me).
- There is a clear path to this steady, highly compensated job: get good grades in high school → go to college → get good grades → get into pharmacy school → get good grades → get job → finally experience happiness.

- I shall, as a seventeen-year-old with no other context or research, from this day forward, dedicate my life to becoming a pharmacist.

Unlike those "silly theater kids getting their useless liberal arts degrees," my education path was set with a job at the end of the tunnel. All I had to do was check the boxes of education in the right order and I would be handsomely rewarded with a satisfying and gratifying career. While it is hard to argue with the fact that yes, I did in fact get a good return on my educational investment, there was a problem with my mindset and path:

There was no flexibility built in.

Now, as I said, I have a certain personality that lends itself well to pharmacy. If you ask my wife about it, she'll probably tell you about the time early in our relationship when I was appalled at her lack of attention to detail regarding food storage. I would always prepare my lunches for the week on Sunday, part of which involved chopping various vegetables. One Sunday, Cassie—you are now on a first name basis with my wife—tried "helping" by slicing some cucumbers and putting them in my lunch container. Only I was appalled, and she was confused, when she had put them in the rectangular container, and NOT the square one.

Me: "Honey, the square container is for cucumbers, why would you put it in the rectangular one?"

Cassie: "Um, they still fit."

Me: "I am having serious doubts about our relationship."

Fortunately, I didn't let a little slip up like that derail our relationship, but it highlighted a legitimate weakness in me: I was too rigid and clearly lacked flexibility.

This rigidness, while often an asset in the "focus on getting stuff done" department, also had a downside in my job as a pharmacist. When I was in pharmacy school and in my pharmacy residency, amidst the chaos of projects, studying, tests, and other various deadlines, I would always tell myself that when I graduated and got my "real job," things would settle down and I would be able to find my happy routine. If you remember my timeline above, the final point was becoming employed and "finally finding that happiness." For those of you reading this who have spent any time in a "real job," I think you know how this story goes.

I had this idea that I would start working, earn that big paycheck, and the clouds would part while the stars lined up as I began my pharmacy career. There would be ample staffing every day. Patients would listen, improve their health, and really appreciate what I was doing for them. All this would occur in an environment with other professionals that supported and respected my role. With this ideal practice environment, I would have a nice "routine" on a daily and weekly basis that I could look forward to regularly.

It did not take long for my dreams of routines and structure to fall apart.

Early in my career, as I jumped into my first clinical pharmacist position, I had figured I could carve out a nice little routine for myself. Unfortunately for my plans, the realities of my job quickly got in the way. Within my first few days on the job, I had a pharmacy student that I was responsible for precepting. Ironically, he had been in the clinic I was in charge of longer than I had, as he was near the end of his six-week rotation and I just starting the beginning of my "no end in sight" job. It didn't seem right for me to precept—I had no rapport with my patients or team that I worked with, I had no concept of how that particular clinic "flow" worked, and I still had my early career/new practitioner doubts. Each day was not only a challenge for me to get through, but with a student, there was an added layer of complexity to navigate. Each patient question was filtered like a game of telephone from the patient, to the student, and finally to me. This added layer of time and complexity only exacerbated my stress in trying to accomplish all my responsibilities daily. I thought that getting my "real world" job meant I could finally leave work at work, whereas I found myself still staying late and catching up on other projects like when I was a pharmacy student and resident. Instead of embracing the unique challenges each day brought, I was trying to mold what was happening into *my* plan and idea of what I thought it *should* be.

Eventually, the student's rotation ended. Now, I don't want to give the impression I don't enjoy teaching and precepting students. Teaching is one of my favorite things to do, and it's why I'm writing this book! *However*, I am using this example to show how flustered and rigid I was in regards to how I imagined work should go versus how it actually did. My expectation of how things should go was not matched by how they actually went, and this was creating a lot of stress and anxiety in me. Once I had finished with the student, I thought the seas would part and *then* my nice, comfy routine would begin. I hope by this point you are realizing that my frustrating experiences would not be over just yet.

Even though my student left, another person was leaving for a few months: one of the pharmacists I worked with had a baby! As a father, I love that our organization provides so much time off for the birth of a child. The other pharmacists work together to help cover the time away for the new parent and our patients still get the care they need. For me, it meant more responsibilities I was not prepared for, and it pushed me closer to the feeling of burnout. My idealistic dream of routine and structure was dealt another blow, and I was not handling it well. Yet again, I was unprepared to deal with the unexpected.

My colleague would return, but my cycle of frustration would continue. Whether it was precepting a challenging pharmacy resident, having a load of new projects and responsibilities given to me, or just dealing with the daily challenges of working in a high stress environment, my self-doubt was high and my ability to cope was low. I was anchored to an idea of structure, and my rigid personality made it challenging for me to adapt.

What is your personality like? Do you deal well with structure? How about the curveballs and unexpected frustrations of your job? I know that many people have difficulty handling when things don't go the way they planned at work. In healthcare, however, this is the default: things will not go as planned, technology will fail, and patients will ignore our plans. There is so much beyond our control, thus the ability to adapt and remain flexible may be as important as the clinical information we learn and apply. The challenge is healthcare attracts a lot of Type A personalities that are able to control a lot about their environment and life . . . up to a certain point. Those who can thrive in the unexpected are those who tend to have more success and enjoyment in healthcare. The ability to "roll with the punches" is important.

How did I learn to embrace the unexpected? It was only after applying the lessons of improvisation that I trained my "flexible" muscle to be stronger. Throughout our healthcare training, there is an obvious emphasis on objective, hard outcomes and data. You cannot perform as a healthcare provider without these hard, measurable skills. That's why things like MD's, PharmD's, and licenses are so important. What isn't taught well are the soft skills, of which improv helps to grow and foster. We are trained to think in a stepwise fashion, often in a controlled environment. When we are forced into uncomfortable or unexpected situations, there are struggles with applying these hard skills.

What I lacked, despite my extensive training in pharmacy, was the ability the handle the unexpected. Improv training forced me to develop the skill of flexibility, as everything done on stage can be considered "unexpected." Improv training provides a safe environment to get into the "flight simulator" of the unexpected. Every moment on stage, in a class, or practicing an exercise is training your mind to remain present in the moment, accept whatever happens, and then respond quickly and intelligently. Yes, I said intelligently, as the best improvers are not the silliest or wackiest or craziest, but the smartest. They learn to relax and remain flexible in the moment, but are able to draw upon their intelligence to generate rich, deep, and interesting scenes.

What I was able to do with improv training was take my "pharmacist brain" and learn to apply the skill of flexibility in stressful and unexpected situations effectively and intelligently. My countless hours on stage listening and reacting helped turn me from a rigid, inflexible pharmacist into a pharmacist able to embrace the chaos of healthcare, able to deliver my information and care to patients appropriately and without the anxiety of being tied to a routine that inevitably would be interrupted.

These days, I've relaxed my rigid ways and I'm proud to say that I now can put whatever vegetable into whatever container. But just don't use a container that's overly large for what it needs to hold. I still have *some* standards for efficiency. However, my ability to adapt to the unexpected and unknown has grown much beyond mere vegetable storage.

Early in my career, all I wanted was to have my clinic, my routine, and my predictability. However, after my "flexibility" brain was developed, I took a position as a "floater." Every day was something new, something unexpected, and something I could not plan for. Each patient was new to me. The provider I was assisting wasn't expecting me. Where I would be covering was often news to me when the clock hit 0800. It was a challenging position, but I thrived in it. Whether it meant driving across town mid-day to cover one of the satellite clinics, spending four months covering for maternity leave, or simultaneously covering three or four pharmacist duties, I was able to handle it. Being a float pharmacist is something I would never have dreamed of early in my career. Yet, years later, I found myself able to thrive in the unexpected.

My hope for others in healthcare is that if a rigid, Type A pharmacist like me can "untrain" his inflexible brain, anybody can. The first step is an attitude shift from our expectations of control to one that embraces the inevitable entropy that will happen. Once we can embrace and understand the unexpected will come, the next step is to apply the improviser "yes, and" mindset. We can learn these "unexpected" problems are gifts, learning opportunities, or inspiration for new ways of innovating: think of all the telehealth progress of COVID-19. If healthcare providers can "yes, and" the unexpected occurrences of their day, a newfound joy can be experienced.

An Unpredictable Canine Distraction

I taught an online workshop for nurses, and it was amazing how quickly they figured out how to prepare for the unpredictable. Two brave volunteers were playing a game called "One Word Story"[17] where they were given a title of a story to tell and the two would go back and forth building this story a single word at a time. The game forces the participants to give up control, live in the moment, and put trust in a stranger—things that healthcare professionals don't always love to do.

---

17. Do you want to give one word story a try? Here is a link to check out a video on how! https://youtu.be/ixds6gbp4Ps

As an added degree of difficulty, this was done virtually via Zoom. Building a story one word at a time with a stranger is hard enough in person, but single word storytelling over the interwebs is another difficulty level.

Fortunately, these two nurses told a beautiful story that had plot twists, plot turns, and, most impressive with this type of story, an actual coherent plot. I always have the participants debrief the activity, to discuss the key takeaways, talk about challenges and successes, and as always, how this would help them in their day jobs of taking care of patients.

Not surprisingly, both the participants said it was fun but difficult to cede control to a single word at a time, and to let the story go where it naturally went rather than force it to where they wanted it to go. This is common feedback, but also why the activity is so valuable. As we were wrapping up, one of the participants hit me with something truly unpredictable when she said. "It was fun, but I got a little distracted because my dog started having a seizure while we were telling the story."

She got an A+ for commitment.

I would have had no idea that she had such a distraction going on. For you animal lovers out there, she said this was not an uncommon occurrence, and her dog was indeed safe. However, it was an excellent example of what we are able to do when the unpredictable happens. She immediately was able to assess the situation, continue with the activity, and most impressively, have fun while doing it.

Who among us has not had something similarly unexpected or distracting occur during our careers? For most, the chaos and unpredictability is an almost daily occurrence, and something far beyond our control. The goals of applying improv training to healthcare are to embrace the chaos we work in, to have empathic interactions despite the challenges we face, and to be more resilient in the face of the inevitable uncertainties we face on a daily basis, something this incredible nurse was able to pull off spectacularly. By incorporating the tools of improvisation, we will have not only the most highly trained healthcare providers in history but the most resilient in the face of volatile situations as well.

Beyond Acceptance: Learn to Love the Curveballs

I want to take a step back to my sports analogy, because I really like baseball. So much so that, if you recall, being a pitcher for the Chicago Cubs was my first choice job when Mrs. Christman, my high school chemistry teacher, asked me what I wanted to do when I grew up. Once she was done laughing, and could see my tears of sadness through her tears of laughter, she suggested I go into something more practical that used acids and bases instead of bats and base hits. My soul was crushed, but my love affair with baseball could never be washed away by the tears of my teacher and myself.

You may wonder why I would enjoy something that, to put it bluntly, is so boring. I will cede baseball doesn't grab the attention as well as a slam dunk in basketball, a Hail Mary in football, or the endless stream of COVID-themed nurse TikTok videos. Yet what I love about baseball is what I also love about improv and healthcare: no two games, scenes, or encounters will be the same. On any given day or night, you can and likely *will* witness something that has never been seen before. As a fan of sports or improv comedy, this is what makes these events so exciting. As a participant in healthcare, it is what can make things so terrifying. But it doesn't have to be! Unpredictability can actually be a positive in healthcare, just as it is in sports and improv.

I can recall as a student and new pharmacist, the fear of a new patient, a curveball question, or a totally random problem that had nothing to do with my clinical training. Early on in my career, wide-eyed and fresh with hard-earned knowledge from school and residency, it wasn't the clinical knowledge that I struggled with. It was the self-doubt of the gray areas, unexpected behaviors, and off-the-wall questions that had me wondering if Mrs. Christman was wise in steering me into the field of pharmacy.

Becoming a trained improviser early in my pharmacy career helped me overcome my self-doubt and thrive in these challenging scenarios.

So, what exactly is it about improv that works?

Improv taught me not merely to accept the unknown, but to *love* it.

I think one of the biggest shifts that improv training provides is the mindset toward the unexpected. Becoming an improviser rewires your brain over time from dreading the unexpected, to tolerating it, and then ultimately to loving it! This mental transformation is especially useful for healthcare professionals, who, at least in my experience, like control. Control of their workflow, their workspace, and their schedule, to name a few. This makes sense as healthcare tends to attract many who fall under the umbrella of a "Type A" personality. Often, this can serve us well in how we approach our respective jobs. However, when this locus of control is broken, the effectiveness of our Type A professional can break down. Learning to embrace the unexpected is a huge benefit to training and thinking like an improviser. Rather than spending precious time and energy fighting to regain control, a healthcare professional that can embrace the reality before them can then spend their energy overcoming the obstacles in their path to providing excellent patient care.

This mindset shift was my first step in letting go of control. If healthcare professionals could simply shift from fighting the unknown to accepting it, we would make huge strides. Yet, a true improv mindset is not simply accepting the unknown, but embracing and using it as a tool to be more effective.

A patient I am calling about diabetes is agitated because his Valium prescription was reduced? Good, I am getting a chance to practice empathy and redirecting to the task at hand.

Laptop needs another thirty minutes to update and reboot? Good. I can use this as an opportunity to practice my own patience and letting go of control.

A patient is inappropriately connected to your extension, interrupting your day with a task that should have been handled by someone else? Good, let's see how well I can troubleshoot and provide an excellent experience.

This mindset shift to embracing the unexpected and unknown is not easy, and it is probably not a regular human habit. In general, we like homeostasis, recognizable patterns, and routines. The pain comes when these routines and patterns are inevitably shattered by the realities of life. With an improv mindset, our "homeostasis" is that the unexpected will happen. So when things don't go as planned, it is paradoxically *exactly* what we would expect.

How to Embrace Uncertainty? Listen and Stay in the Moment

When the unexpected pops up, do you feel like closing your eyes, putting your fingers in your ears, and imagining you were anywhere but in that unexpected moment? If so, don't worry. You likely have a lot of company. Heck, I may have even seen you there in warm, cozy, and fictitious "Anywhere-but-heresville." However, if we want to embrace and overcome the unexpected, there are two skills that are crucial: listening intently and actually staying *in* the moment.

Applying these skills of improv to the healthcare game are particularly effective in being able to respond quickly yet constructively. I am not sure you are aware of this, but we don't get a ton of time to see patients. Primary care providers get mere minutes to diagnose and treat complex health issues. Nurses have seemingly endless tasks from checking vitals to administering medications at all hours. Pharmacists famously fill hundreds of prescriptions a day in community pharmacies.

Simply performing these time-restricted tasks by themselves is a tall order. But it is never just the "one thing." There are phone calls that interrupt, family members insisting to get the latest update on their loved one, and those pesky Code Blues that often turn out to be nothing more than an incorrect button being pressed. (Something I have become fond of calling "Code Blue Balls.") Regardless if a Code is real or just a Code Tease, it interrupts a healthcare professional's ability to focus and take are of their duties.

In short, much is asked of us. And it is also asked of us to perform it with a high level of service, compassion, and empathy, as it should be.

One issue that will trip up new improvisers, and new healthcare providers, is that they will try to "think" their way through a scene. They will spend their effort trying to conjure up what they believe is the funniest line, idea, or premise. Unfortunately, while they are stewing in their own comedic brain juices, they are completely missing the action on stage. What often happens is that their wonderful comedic idea is obsolete by the time their scene partner finishes their line. The response may be quick, as they have been thinking about it, but it will not be effective.

This back and forth of listening and responding is the same game that is played in a patient encounter. Unfortunately, often the same mistakes are made by the healthcare provider—they'll sit in their own head, coming up with an idea or plan, all the while missing critical information a patient is trying to convey to them. As they have limited time with their patients, the response may be swift, but it was preloaded before they had even heard the patient speak. The plan may come quickly, but it will not be as effective had they been listening in the moment.

When a response is preloaded like this, the patient doesn't feel heard. Nobody likes getting stepped on, ignored, and bulldozed in a conversation. Unfortunately, our patients *do* feel like this a lot of the time. Their big time concerns are brushed over for what *we* feel is more important. While we may have a clinical reason that "our" idea truly is more important, if we don't heed our patients' words and worries, our "important" idea will be ignored.

A way to overcome the unexpected while increasing patient engagement comes back to the idea of "yes, and." Just listen and build together. A relationship with a patient should be a two-way partnership where concerns and wishes from both sides are considered, discussed, and ultimately resolved to at least some semblance of satisfaction from both sides. What usually happens, however, is that the healthcare provider ignores the concerns of the patients, or dismisses their idea as "odd" or "from the internet" and continues on. This leaves the patient feeling frustrated, ignored, and ultimately disengaged.

A patient I was following for blood pressure came to me complaining of headaches. He had been started on hydralazine by another provider, despite having explained to them that this medicine caused headaches previously. Well, when he got into my office, I asked him how he was doing with the newest addition to his blood pressure medication. A slammed hand on the desk and some choice four letter bombs later, I found out that hydralazine *still* was causing him headaches. By proxy of this situation, hydralazine was giving me a headache, too.

He went on to opine, "You people never listen to me. You have your fancy white coats and degrees, but I am the one who is suffering. Why can't you get it through your heads that I am sensitive to medication."

A default, and poor choice in this case, answer might be to explain that we have degrees, years of experience, and thus, we *know* what is best for the patient. Objectively, we probably do and is likely a reflex response. However, nobody knows the patient better than the patient. If they get headaches from hydralazine, maybe we should stop trying it.

So, I "yes, anded" the situation. I said something along the lines of, "Yes, I hear you, and it sucks to not be listened to. A lot of providers do a very poor job of listening to patients, and trust me, you are not the first patient to complain about this." See what I did? I turned the argument to "the man." "So," I said, "let's find a solution. We need to control your blood pressure and also make sure you can tolerate the medicines. It's a balance we need to find, together. What if we tried something else you haven't done before, and see if your blood pressure and headaches improve?"

The patient got on board, he was engaged, and by the end of the appointment, he was telling me about a giant motorcycle rally in South Dakota where his brother had gotten him front row passes to a bunch of hard rockin' bands. He was smiling. He was engaged in his care. I don't claim to be a healthcare hero, but all it took was "yes, anding" his reality, his complaint, and his frustration.

The skill of listening intently in the moment helps us to respond quickly and effectively while engaging our patients as well. The problems our patients present can often be answered if we can get out of our own head and just listen and respond. The good news is that unlike a cardiology fellowship, a surgical residency, or a wait for your prescription, it does not have to take a long time to become better at embracing the unknown and providing quick and constructive responses.

One way to develop these skills is to take an improv class or maybe even a workshop with someone who specializes in applying improv to healthcare like yours truly. If you are just too excited and can't wait that long, you can start today by practicing listening to your significant other, friends, or other loved ones. If something unexpected occurs, rather than curse the change in fortune, think of what new opportunity has been provided to you. When someone you care about comes to you with a problem, rather than having a solution in your head ready to go before hearing them, focus all your energy on what they are saying and simply respond. The more you practice, the better you will become at these translatable improv skills. At first, I will admit, it is a challenge, especially to embrace the unexpected occurrence. You may not be good at it. Give it time, and with enough repetitions and practice, your embrace of the unknown and quick and effective response will become second nature, whether you are talking to your spouse, a patient, or a stranger that just sat down next to you on a flight with a Filet O' Fish and a large order of onion rings.

Chapter 5

HONESTY

Not Just for Politicians

Finding Truth from Comedy

When you think of great comedians, do you think of them being great truth tellers? One of the often surprising underlying principles in great improv, and great comedy, is that it must come from a place of truth or reality. I have both seen and participated in improv scenes that started off in a wild land I refer to as "crazytown," that were neither great nor comedic. Scenes that start off in "crazytown" often do so because the players are "trying really hard" to make jokes, or make comedy happen with too many odd things happening at once. Like a seemingly normal scene between two lumberjacks can quickly evolve (or would it be devolve?) into a place where the trees are teleporting the lumberjacks to outer space to fight off alien space invaders who have come to steal the recipe for Coca Cola. Despite working "extra hard" to be funny, these scenes are often the least funny. Why is that?

As I mentioned above, great comedy and improv must come from a place of truth. Think of why *Seinfeld* or *The Office* work so well. We've all met a "George Costanza," and we've all worked with a "Dwight Schrute." They are "real" characters, based in a simple and believable setting, and whatever happens is explored and heightened. Think about some of the shows you know that didn't make it through their first season. Was there a "wacky" shtick? Was the show based on an unbelievable premise? Was the main character wildly over the top? It would not surprise me if the answer to any of these questions is yes.

When a scene or show starts off too far-fetched to have any grounding in reality, it has already hit its high point, it has nowhere to go or, as we say, "heighten." Whatever the interesting or funny thing about a scene, an episode, or a character is, there has to be some base in reality so that the odd or funny thing can be highlighted and contrasted against it, built, and eventually reach a high point. Think of the oft used term "jump the shark," which means to "reach a point at which far-fetched events are included merely for the sake of novelty, indicative of a decline in quality."[18] It references the TV show *Happy Days* and an episode where the main character jumps over a shark while waterskiing. At that point, *Happy Days* had reached a point of being able to "heighten" no more and so they had to reach for a novelty so far-fetched that it was, despite it being a fictional show, unbelievable.

In our culture, TV shows, politicians, and other celebrities are referenced to "jump the shark," and it usually means

---

18. *Lexico*, s.v. "jump the shark," accessed 2 July 2020, https://www.lexico.com/en /definition/jump_the_shark.

that we stop paying attention to them. Well, I remember this section started talking about applying improv principles to healthcare, and dammit, I am bringing it all around, I promise.

Our healthcare system has "jumped the shark," "gone to crazytown," and lost the engagement of its employees.

I am writing this as a citizen of the good ol' US of A where there is a large dichotomy in the amount we spend, the way we treat our healthcare workers, and our health outcomes. We have the highest per capita spending, and an obesity rate to match.[19] We tout pharmacists as "the most trusted healthcare providers," but then ask them to sell cigarettes, candy, and booze to go along with their nicotine gum, insulin, and benzodiazepines. We can't call our nurses heroes enough: we give them a whole week of recognition while rewarding them with stale breadsticks, room-temperature pizza, and a bag of "salad" from the store. (Thanks to my wife for the insight on that "prize" for being a nurse.) So, they seriously do yeoman's work and get a big poop sandwich for their efforts.

Is it any wonder that those that practice within our healthcare system find it hard and are often disengaged?

We need our healthcare system to get back to reality. We need it to be honest with those that practice within it. How is that possible?

Here comes that sweet, sweet improv philosophy to the rescue. What makes improv great is how it is based in reality,

19. Statista Research Department, "Per capita health expenditure in selected countries 2018," *statista*, 8 September 2021, https://www.statista.com/statistics/236541/per-capita-health-expenditure-by-country.

how it is brutally honest at times, and how it doesn't try to deceive the audience. I think we in healthcare feel at least a little deceived because we expected to be saving lives, but instead we are saving the bottom line of keyboard makers by typing into a computer all day long. Here's an idea that could change how we feel about our jobs in healthcare:

What if CEOs, managers, and administrators were just . . . honest?

What if they honestly explained that their job is to make money for the [insert hospital, pharmacy, clinic] *while administering health care?*" I am an "ugly capitalist," and don't see the problem of a highly trained medical professional making a comfortable living by spending years training to do a demanding, stressful, and often thankless job. However, I do see a problem when our system pretends that their sole and noble cause is taking care of sick people. It is dishonest to those who provide care, and to those who receive it.

Now, the part about fixing the profit model of healthcare, administering it more efficiently, and keeping costs to patients more reasonable? That is probably not within the scope of this book, so I'll keep my focus on a humbler goal. We have a serious engagement and honesty problem in healthcare, and while we need to get several steps down the road to better solutions, we have to be willing to take the first step and be honest with our practitioners.

One way to go about tackling this honesty and engagement problem is to start grounding our healthcare in a more realistic place, which in itself is an improv move. There is obviously a disconnect from those of us in "the trenches" and those who are "in charge." The disconnect seems to come from the unrealistic expectations from above to those who feel that they're doing the actual work of healthcare, making difficult decisions, working long hours, and putting themselves in harm's way. Our personal expectations of ourselves on the ground is very high, but despite these high expectations, it does not meet what is demanded of us.

We want to provide exceptional, personable, and adequate care to our patients. To us, this means sometimes taking more time, using a non-traditional resource, or trying a treatment that is either not standard of care, or billable for reimbursement. Oftentimes, we are met with resistance when we color outside the lines of what is expected of us. The pushback on us is frustrating, disheartening, and puzzling when we thought we were all working for the same team to take care of patients.

By applying the shared reality that improvisation preaches, our goal would be to share each of our personal preferences and expectations. Then, and here is where the "doing" is more important than the "discussing," both sides of this thing need to establish an honest reality that both are able to live with. I was going to write "happy with," but some of the best deals are when both sides are left wanting a little more. This shared reality would also foster engagement from healthcare providers, as they will be able to see the "why" of what they are doing from the other side, and perhaps more importantly, be more committed to the organization's cause if their desires are met at least halfway.

Be Honest with Our Patients

Despite our greatest intentions, best efforts, and high investment in resources, our healthcare interventions are far from perfect. Sometimes a procedure goes poorly and a patient is left in worse condition than when they started. Sometimes an image is misinterpreted. Sometimes, a medication can cause an adverse drug reaction. These outcomes are the unfortunate reality of well-intentioned but imperfect healthcare interventions that are essentially our "best guess." Yet, I wonder if our patients are truly aware of the imperfect nature of the practice of medicine.

As a pharmacist, I can only claim to be an expert on medications and their possible side effects. So, whenever a patient asks me if a medication will potentially cause a side effect, I am honest with them. I tell them the most common and most serious potential side effects, but then offer a disclaimer of honesty and humility when dealing with such complex chemical structures combined with the human body. I let them know that this is my best guess, but I cannot promise you won't have these, or other side effects. My caveat is that I tell them this information is not meant to scare them, but so that they pay attention to any changes that happen once they take their medication.

Some may argue this will discourage patients from taking their medications. Yet, I find the most common response I get is "Thank you," with a follow up that can be paraphrased as "I'd rather know something could happen than be surprised."

Whether it's a pill or surgical procedure, our patients deserve to have honest discussions about risks versus benefits. I think we get a little too cocky and provide too much in the way of absolutes to patients in the form of "This will definitely work" to "This is totally safe." There are no absolutes in healthcare, and even the most seemingly mundane procedure or medication could have an unwanted outcome. We don't get to control these outcomes, but we can provide honest explanations to our patients.

When it Comes to Healthcare and Football, I Am Tired of Punting, and So Are Our Patients

Grounding our healthcare in a place of reality with our patients is another way to keep them engaged. The term "punt" is common in healthcare, with patients being "punted" or sent to multiple different appointments and specialties only to be "punted" or sent back to a different one with no real progress being made or improvements in the patient's condition. This back and forth leaves patients frustrated and disengaged. It reminds me of a dear patient of mine whom I have followed for their blood sugar. They are someone we in healthcare might call a "high utilizer" and who requires a lot of extra TLC. For this patient, it meant a nearly endless list of problems, conditions, and, near and dear to my heart, medication allergies.

While the focus with this patient was supposed to be on their diabetes, our appointments inevitably became a long discussion about the medications they needed, were missing, or that were causing them problems. On one particular occasion, they brought up their concern that their new heartburn medication was no longer effective. The very—this is a heavy dose of sarcasm—obvious reason was that the color had changed on the capsule. A change in the contract for the preferred generic manufacturer, something well beyond my control, was to blame for the change in appearance.

They had been receiving the different colored pill for a few months and had noticed their heartburn worsened. I am not here to debate if this was truly due to the new brand of pill being less potent. I am an improviser, and say "yes, and" and accept reality. That this new pill wasn't working was my patient's reality.

To complicate the situation, they had been admitted to the hospital within the previous few weeks and had received their old style of heartburn medication. For some reason, our inpatient pharmacy had not gotten the fresh new generic manufactured pill. The good news is that when they were in the hospital, their heartburn was controlled. The bad news is they now thought our organization "had" their preferred pill and that we should be able to easily supply it.

Unfortunately, this was not the truth, and they had already spoken to their provider who had spoken, according to my patient, with someone in the outpatient pharmacy who said we would be able to supply their brand. It was no secret amongst pharmacy staff that we were at the whims of national contracts for generic medications, and the decision as to which manufacturer we used was so far beyond all of our pay grades that it was simply impossible to promise a particular looking pill.

Now my patient, with the assurance of their provider, was under the impression we could get their specific pill and fix their heartburn and was on the phone with me asking why they still had heartburn and didn't have their preferred pill.

As much as it hurt, it was time for someone to be honest with them, and that someone, as you may have guessed, was me.

I listened intently to their story, expressed a shared frustration over the miscommunication that we could get their specific pill. Then I gave them the straight truth:

"We cannot get your specific pill. The decision for what we get is made on a national level and is totally beyond our control. I am sorry you were told otherwise, but we need to figure out a solution for you, which may mean an alternative medication."

Rather than use your imagination, I will tell you they were less than pleased. Yet they were also grateful I had been honest with them. The story does have a happy ending though. Since the patient realized our organization did not have the power to fix the pill problem, they got to work solving it. They researched what manufacturer they had been using when it was effective, and made calls to other pharmacies until they found one that had the brand they wanted. Then, they let me and their provider know what pharmacy had it, and their provider was able to call in their prescription.

Problem solved. No more heartburn. The patient's heartburn symptoms presumably improved as well.

That is just one example of how we can utilize the improv tenet of honesty to engage our patients and solve their problems. Or, in this case, get the patient to help solve the problem for themself!

Chapter 6

COMMUNICATION

*Yes, Improving Healthcare
Can Be This Simple*

Communicate Clearly and Specifically

Which of these statements paints a clearer picture?

Statement A: Hand me that soda.

Statement B: If you don't hit me with an ice-cold Mountain Dew Code Red right now, I am gonna straight crash.

I am hopeful that Statement B gave a much more vivid picture of what could be happening with a hypothetical soda request. Statement A is bland, vanilla, and very vague. Statement B sounds like it came straight from someone who has been up for hours and is in desperate need of some icy cold caffeinated refreshment STAT. (By the way, the correct answer to both requests is . . . don't drink soda. It's sugary poison.)

When I am performing an improv scene, the more specific I am with the details of the scene, the more rich and entertaining that scene is. This is so for a number of reasons. From an audience perspective, you are painted a much more vivid picture and thus feel more connection, excitement, and emotional investment in the scene. From a performer perspective, the more detail a scene partner can give me, the more information I have to draw on for inspiration on what that scene could be about, more information to react, and more details about who that improvised character is on stage.

If you have not picked up on it yet, improvisation requires a lot of communication skills, and if you aren't able to communicate, you are generally not going to find much success as an improviser.

However, to work in healthcare, is there a licensing exam on communication? Can pharmacists or physicians get board certified in "specific counseling with patients"? As of 2020, the answer is no, and my guess is it'll be like that long into the future as well. We have brilliant doctors, nurses, pharmacists, and many other disciplines that have more knowledge in the tip of their finger than I have in my entire brainstem (anatomy and physiology were not my strongest subjects). Unfortunately, many can't get the brilliant ideas and information in their head out of their mouths in a way that others (1) understand or (2) care about it.

What are brilliant yet inept communicators to do?

Apply these improvisation principles and watch their personal and patient satisfaction soar! (Are you tired of me asking you so many questions throughout the book? Well, are ya?!)

The first step in communicating more clearly is to admit we could have a problem. Based on the number of medical mistakes that are due to a lack of communication, the number of problems I have had to fix because of a miscommunication, and the amount of time we all probably waste because of a lack of communication, I think it is safe to say: we have a communication problem.

Cool, doesn't that feel better to admit?

Alright, we have admitted we have a problem. The next step is to be open to the suggestions and yes, even criticism that is a-comin' your way. It's out of love, I promise. It's also out of frustration. Sorry, it's not all love.

One rule I'd like you to take away from this section is the importance of clearly communicating your "Base Reality," as we say in improv. Your base reality is just your "who, what, and where." It is very simple. But it is, at least in my experience, not that easy.

"Augmentin for window pickup, please."

This was the Skype message I received from a physician in our clinic, asking me to process an urgent antibiotic for a patient that was waiting. This was actually better than they normally communicated. At least we weren't going to mail a prescription, taking several days for a patient with an acute infection. The downside to this attempt at being proactive was that a key element was left out.

Do you see what I didn't have?

If you have magical healthcare mindreading ability, then you are likely wondering what the hell my problem with this provider was. If you are a mere mortal such as myself, you are likely realizing the "afterthought" was who this patient was that needed an antibiotic. I understand these kinds of things happen. This "mistake" was not the first time this provider had been known to leave out a key part of a communication, and they were not always back at their Skype window to sort out the issue. The patients would then go to our pharmacy to pick up the prescription that had been promised to be ready by the doctor, not see their name, wait to "talk" to a member of our outpatient pharmacy staff, and then become indignant about how we "didn't know how to do our jobs."

The patient wasn't wrong. This whole fiasco could have been avoided with a simple sharing of our "base reality" and basic information.

Have I mentioned how much training our already-smart people have gotten? And the older I get, the newer ones coming in are only getting smarter. *But*, I think we forget how important it is to perform simple tasks. Getting the "who, what, and where" out to be clear and specific in your communication, will help avoid so much of our frustration.

In my own career, getting this basic yet crucial information out at the beginning of appointments helps to clear up a lot of confusion that I will see. Many of my patient interactions start off a little something like this:

"I thought I was here to see the doctor. Why am I seeing the pharmacist?"

My job as a pharmacist is pretty unique in that I get to practice disease state management under a collaborative practice agreement.

Not sure exactly what that means? No sweat. I have been explaining what an Ambulatory Care Clinical Pharmacy Specialist does to my parents for years, and they still don't understand that I don't actually "count pills in the back." So, when a patient comes into my office to discuss their diabetes or high blood pressure, they are confused as to why they are seeing a pharmacist, I don't take it personally. Admittedly, I used to in the past . . . just a little bit at least. I mean, c'mon, who wouldn't be at least a little bit offended after training seven years, passing multiple tests, and demonstrating enough trust to be able to prescribe as a pharmacist?

However, this attitude didn't serve me well in trying to serve patients well. All of us, no matter our training, will encounter a scenario where the patient either doesn't know *why* they are seeing you or *care* how many years you spent training. My nurse practitioner wife is the proud owner of three degrees and also gets her share of confused patients who "thought they were seeing a real doctor."

Whether you are a PharmD, MD, or NP, being clear and specific at the top of your appointment is crucial for a successful interaction. It is the same "base reality" idea as an improv scene. While seemingly super basic, just getting out the *who* (your title, position), *what* (urgent care visit or annual wellness check), and *why* (blood pressure check or to refill medications) can work wonders. *Where* is probably not needed in an office setting but getting to the *why* of an appointment is important.

Let's use me as an example because I am writing this book and you seemed interested enough to read it. When I am seeing a new patient, it goes a little something like this:

"Hello, nice to meet you. My name is Cory and I am the pharmacist that works with Dr. X. They saw you last month and were really concerned about your blood sugar control. They referred you into our pharmacy clinic because here at our office, pharmacists can see you just like doctors can, adjust your diabetes medications, and help to get your blood sugar back under control. I know seeing a pharmacist is not something you have probably done before, but we can see you more frequently than the doctor, so we can spend more time taking care of you than if you had to wait to see them again. Thanks again for coming in today, so let's start by going over what medications you are taking . . ."

A couple of observations. First, this may seem quite long, but providing the patient my background, how they ended up in my office, and the purpose of our visit helps to set the stage for the clinical portion of our visit. By getting this information out, the patient is hopefully on board with seeing me instead of the doctor and doesn't spend our entire appointment secretly wondering when the "real" doctor is coming in to see them. Perhaps it helps to ease their fear that an "unqualified" person is seeing them instead of their doctor. I also like to add a little extra "something" for the patient. In this case, it's to be honest that I can see them more often than their doctor, especially when a huge source of dissatisfaction is appointment wait times.

A second observation: you may be thinking, "No shit, Cory. Of course we're supposed to tell patients what our visit is about."

Thank you for that observation. I will take it to heart. (I might even write a book and put that tidbit in it.) I will also reply that despite this being "basic" knowledge, I can't tell you how many appointments I have been in where the provider just jumps right into the problems, medications, or medical questions. Now, I get it. Time is a factor, and we all wish we had more of it to spend with our patients. Unfortunately, if we can't make these simple connections and get this information out at the top, our time just might be wasted.

It reminds me of an improv scene I was watching. A team from out of town had come to our theater as a guest to perform. We promoted it. Our theater was excited to have them. However, in one of their scenes, I noticed something peculiar and uncomfortable. This group of three had been improvising for about two minutes, yet a few things had not happened: there had been no laughs, and more tellingly, there was no idea of who these three characters were to each other. Each team member nervously looked at the other one to see if someone would help figure out what was happening in the scene. There was a doctor, but we didn't know their name, and it was also happening at a party . . . until another team member contradicted that location. It was two minutes of what felt like grasping for feathers in a windstorm at night with no productive end (which probably is what a typical doctor's appointment feels like for a patient, except longer).

They had no base reality and their scene suffered because of it. Eventually, and mercifully, they ended the scene and moved on to something different. There was a lesson to be learned from that scene for both improvisation and healthcare: you gotta get your who, what, and where/why out at the top, otherwise anything that follows is going to be confusing and wasted time.

Do the simple things well, and the great things shall follow.

Make the Who, What, and Where Evident

I am a clinical pharmacist and so I feel pretty comfortable navigating an often confusing and frustrating healthcare system as a consumer. I am well versed in "medical jargon." I can empathize with staff when they have a full waiting room, the phones won't stop ringing, and the provider is running late. I get it.

That's why I wasn't too concerned about an abdominal ultrasound my primary care provider ordered for me. It was simple: they put in the referral, the imaging center called me, and I made the appointment to get my insides looked at. Easy Peasy. The medical assistant checking me out explained to me I would get a call, and then I could schedule and go on in, nothing special about it.

Surprisingly, things went according to plan. I got a call the next week from the imaging center to schedule my abdominal ultrasound, so I did. I asked if there was anything

I needed for my appointment, and they just said to bring in my insurance card. Easy Peasy.

As my appointment date approached, my double-checking pharmacist personality pushed me to call the imaging center to confirm my appointment and make sure there weren't any other special instructions I needed. So, I called, confirmed my Friday at 7:30 a.m. appointment and asked if there was anything else I needed to know. "Make sure to bring your insurance card." Easy Peasy.

I arrived fifteen minutes early for my appointment, brought that insurance card, and checked in. They even brought me back early. Things were going great! Easy . . . oh you get it.

I met the technician who was going to perform the ultrasound, she introduced herself, explained what she was going to do/need me to do. She did an outstanding job of creating a "base reality" for our appointment. Just before she went to jelly up my belly, she said, "And just to make sure, I am sure you didn't have anything to eat or drink this morning."

Um. Yes, I had a nice intake of water. I asked if that was a problem. She said, "It might be. You were not supposed to have *anything* to eat or drink. We can do it, or we can reschedule."

Remember that part where I had conversations with a medical assistant at my primary care office, and two phone calls with the imaging center about this appointment and the most important piece of information they gave me was "insurance card"? How could information so vital to the actual procedure be missed? Yet, it had, and now I had to choose between rescheduling and maybe having an "improper study."

I rolled the dice, had the scan, and there were no issues with it. I was left pondering several questions.

If I, a ruggedly handsome member of our healthcare system, could have trouble with the instructions for a simple procedure, what is it like for those who have low health literacy, or multiple medical issues, or hearing issues, or any number of other confounders? How many other expensive, time-consuming, or more complex procedures are done incorrectly or rescheduled because we can't communicate clearly and specifically? How many people have been injured or killed because we can't be clear about what is needed or expected of a procedure?

It's clear we have a problem communicating effectively. Improvisation trains us to clearly communicate. And quickly, since there's no time to waste words in an improv scene. While it seems universal and basic to simply communicate who we are, what we are doing, and why we are doing it, it's clear we are failing ourselves and thus our patients. By adapting the simple improv principle of clear communication, we will take better care of our patients.

Be a Better "New Guy"

Clear communication is even more important when you are not working with your regular patients. Picture your favorite restaurant or bar. Then think of the people who serve you, take care of you, and, by default, have gotten to know you over the time you have spent at their establishment. Recall how comforting and familiar it is to walk into a place and have the staff know your name, ask how your family is doing, not even have to ask you for what you want to eat that day. Human beings love homeostasis. It's a state of biological bliss.

With that in mind, now think of the last time your "regular" person was not there. That you found out they moved, or got promoted, or, worse, fired. How did you treat the "FNG"? ("FUN new guy," right?) Was it as pleasant as with your regular? Did you harbor secret resentment? Did you take longer to return to that place of business, lest they keep getting rid of all the "best" people?

We don't, in general, like change, and we especially don't like unexpected change. Now let's swap out someone bringing you lunch with someone holding your life in their hands. Feeling anxious that your normal person isn't there? Thinking about rescheduling? If so, don't feel guilty. It's just a natural reaction.

What was the point of this exploration of changing from the norm? Well, it was to relate it to what I have done for a lot of my pharmacy career: float. I have worked as a per diem float pharmacist in a retail pharmacy as well as a gap pharmacist in our ambulatory care clinics. My entire day was predicated on disappointing patients who had grown accustomed to "their" pharmacist. It was also an interesting look into someone's psyche when I would call and start by asking, "Is Mr. Smith there?" and hear an excited, "Yes, you got him!" This is followed by, "Thanks, I am calling from the VA, my name is Cory, and I am a pharmacist calling for your appointment this morning." Then there's the panicked response of, "What did you do with Danielle? Is she okay? Did you hurt her? I'll hurt you if you did anything to her! Why isn't she there? Are you a pharmacist or just a 'student' because I don't want to talk to a student. Are you qualified? What makes you qualified?"

I knew I was in for a fun appointment.

There were two roads I could travel with each patient, and this was every day, and almost every patient. I got good at disappointing patients by not being their regular. The first road was one of being offended and adversarial, defending "my honor" as a pharmacist and objectively competent healthcare provider. I have seen this before, and it does not end well. It usually devolves into an argument about the merits of the provider's credentials, and I can assure you *that* definitely doesn't end with a patient getting excellent care.

The other road to travel was one inspired by improv: to communicate clearly and specifically, and to "yes, and" their surprise and frustration. This road usually led to reasonable expectations of the visit, assurance that the "regular" was just fine, and a more enjoyable experience for both the patient and for myself. The key is clearly defining at the very beginning my who, what, and where/why for the patient. For example:

"Yes, Mr. Smith, I know that you have been working with Kendrick for a long time on your blood sugars. He is not able to come in today, and I am very sorry, because he is one of the best pharmacists I work with." It's true, Kendrick knows his shit and patients love him. "The good news is he and I are close friends, and we have a very similar approach to diabetes management. So, if you are still alright with me pinch hitting for him today, I'd love to keep up the hard work that you and he have been doing, and then we can get you back to him after today. How does that work?"

In this example, typical of how I normally interact with patients, I empathize with patients accustomed to their normal provider and show understanding that their health is important. I also like to make a personal connection to their "normal person" and emphasize working together, even though I am not their usual provider. Also, I try to understand that some people don't want a fill-in, so I will provide the option to either decline me or take a later date with the person they like.

In our course of treating patients, it is inevitable that we will end up covering for an unfamiliar patient. In these circumstances, by employing the clear communication and base reality tenets of improvisation, you will be able to quickly convey to a patient that you are there to assist them. Inevitably, you will encounter patients who are not as open to seeing you compared to their normal healthcare provider. However, by being clear and upfront at the top of the appointment and providing your "base reality," you will be able to get more out the interview than if you vaguely begin without addressing a patient's possible concern about seeing "the new guy."

Build Team Rapport through Communication

Being able to clearly communicate within a diverse team is critical for success in healthcare. It is often the simple tasks that are not conveyed correctly that can add stress, increase cost, and lead to frayed relationships within a team. One such example of communication gone wrong occurred when I was working on my schedule with one of our medical assistants. A particular Friday had been completely blocked off my schedule for reasons unknown to me. I, being the caring pharmacist that I am, wanted to make sure I had as much availability to see patients, especially since as this scenario unfolded, my wife was days away from delivering our second child. Another pharmacist would be covering for me, but they would not be there as frequently as I normally would, and I wanted to get as many patients seen before my "baby sabbatical."

I sent an email to our medical assistant requesting a single day, Friday, June 12, be reopened for me to see patients. This was clearly communicated. Or so I thought. Within mere minutes, I received a reply saying that the task had been completed. I checked our scheduling tool and that Friday was open. Well done team!

As I looked ahead to my time off, I noticed on the schedule that every Friday had been opened up. They had all been previously blocked off, as my coverage was going to be limited. This fact brought a twinge of panic (pharmacists panic over the smallest things) and a touch of frustration. For many, it could have been a moment of blame and frustration with our scheduler. However, I looked back on my email and I, the great improviser/pharmacist, had said please open up Friday for patients. Oops. Dr. Improv had not communicated specifically and precisely.

So, rather than get frustrated at the scheduler's lack of mind reading ability, I quickly drafted an email profusely apologizing for the miscommunication and requesting the proper single date being opened. The scheduler was understanding, appreciative, and prompt in fixing my mistake.

The ability to communicate clearly is not just important for communicating information and details, but also for making clear when a something was *not* communicated well. In a team, this is important for developing rapport and trust. At the time of this incident, I was the new pharmacist for the clinic. It was especially important to communicate my mistake and apologize so I could develop rapport and a reputation as a team member who is easy to work with. A team that can apply the improv tenet of clearly communicated tasks will be one that can work together more effectively.

Call Out "The Game"

Sometimes in an improv scene, a funny thing happens, but one of the performers on stage misses it. It happens to the best of us, no matter how much hardcore listening we try to employ. But the scene will fall apart if one of the team doesn't understand the key part of the scene, also known at "The Game of the Scene." Improv is a team sport, so if I say a line that is hilarious and clarifies what the funny thing in the scene is about, and my scene partner misses it, then it is my responsibility to help them realize that we just missed something. This reminder of what is funny is much better than one performer, after the show is over, pouting and complaining about the other performer missing that great premise.

The idea of calling out "The Game" is relevant in the world of clear communication and specificity. In an improv scene, we need a method to highlight the funny "game" so that it can easily be identified and explored further. The solution is elegantly, almost insultingly, simple: We just repeat back the thing that was "funny."

The performer appreciates it, because they now have the fodder to play and focus their scene and comedy, and the audience appreciates it because they now know exactly what to laugh at. It's a true win-win.

Recall my hilarious scene about the mall cop/first responders. An example of calling the game out might go something like this:

Mall Security Guard: "Alright, it's first responder happy hour! Great to see you EMT, policeman, and firefighter. It's great to have a place to relax, decompress, and talk shop with other stressful professions like myself, a mall security guard."

Policeman: "So, you think that you, a mall security guard armed with nothing more than a walkie talkie and a Segway, are in the same league of danger as a police, firefighters, and EMT?"

In this case, we are calling out the contrast of what first responders typically deal with, and the realities of a relatively safe and unexciting job as a mall security guard. The repetition helps make it clear for all involved what the rest of this scene will be about—comparing the different professions. It focuses the comedy and allows for a deeper, richer, and funnier scene.

Circling back to healthcare, when a patient comes in with a vague complaint or symptom, it is important for us to repeat and focus so that we know exactly what the patient is thinking and wanting from the appointment. Much like the example above, clearly communicating what the issue at hand is can be as simple as repeating back to clarify to the patient what they think or want the appointment to be about. This is simple, but often overlooked, and highly effective.

By repeating back what the patient says, we are able to clearly define what the patient said in case it was not what the patient had actually meant. This gets the patient engaged in their care by having to listen to us tell them what we thought they were concerned about, thus highlighting the important part of the appointment.

As I have hopefully convinced you, the improv practice of clear communication and specificity is not complex, but it is often overlooked in healthcare. By applying these improv skills to healthcare, we will cut down on errors, increase patient engagement, and find our visits to be more focused and productive.

Listen Intently

How good a listener are you? First, answer that question. Now go ask your spouse, significant other, or any family member. How'd that go? Hopefully you are, in fact, a great listener! If so, congratulations! If not, this chapter should help explain the why and how of listening intently.

If you remember back to the JAMA article I referenced, "Practices to Foster Physician Presence and Connection with patients in the clinical encounter," one of their recommendations was to "listen intently and completely." So this idea of listening intently is backed by the literature and is put into practice as an improviser.

Now, when I say "listen intently," what exactly do I mean? Let's start off with a quote from actor (and retired United States Marine—how's that for some trivia?) Rob Riggle:

> "Listening. I think that's the key. When you improvise, you put a lot of pressure on yourself to create, and to be generating information, and trying to be funny, but if you just listen to what's being said to you, and then react honestly, you generally get better results."

Listening intently means to be totally focused in the moment, be ready to take in whatever is said or done, and then provide an honest response. At the theater where I trained, Tucson Improv Movement, we have a phrase, "Listen with Paranoia." It means that we have to be on our metaphorical and literal toes to receive whatever is said to us. In an improv scene, rather than trying hard to *make* something funny, you just open yourself up to listening intently and reacting honestly. That approach is the most effective way to generate great improv comedy rather than getting stuck in your head making up a joke.

If we can listen intently, we will be at our best on stage.

This also rings true as we take care of patients in a healthcare setting. I'd like to take a piece of that Rob Riggle quote and focus in on it:

> "If you just listen to what's being said to you, and then react honestly, you generally get better results."

The phenomenon of overthinking that we sometimes refer to as "getting in your head" on the improv stage is not just true in comedy, I have had it happen to me as a pharmacist. We can get in our own heads, suffer "paralysis by analysis." Usually, the way we try to get out of it is thinking harder and longer. However, sometimes the answer is as simple as *listening*. We can get so wrapped up in the possible treatment plan or diagnosis we want to implement for a patient that we just forget to listen to them. Unfortunately, when we neglect to listen intently, we often miss the answer that is staring us right in the face the entire time.

I recently had this happen with a patient that was referred to me because they didn't want to take many of their medications. Already, I had identified a want, so I had that going for me. The curious issue with this particular patient was that he wasn't on an absurdly high number of medications. Maybe my view is biased because I see patients with medication lists that top out in the multiple dozens, but this patient was "only" prescribed six medications, and taking three of them. The medications he was taking were for his blood pressure and blood sugar, which was at least a reasonable priority, but he was skipping one other relatively important cholesterol medication.

He said that taking that many medications made him feel overwhelmed, and then he would get depressed about needing to take his medications, then just stop them all out of frustration. I was stuck in my head, thinking about why he was so overwhelmed by a seemingly small number of medications. However, I then realized the importance of the advice I am giving you in this book: I started to listen, and the solutions came.

The patient noted he did not like the idea of being stuck on so many medications for the rest of his life. The root of his issue wasn't the number of medications themselves but the seemingly lifelong sentence of taking them. "Fortunately" for him, they were for the cluster of lifestyle diseases that plague so much of the modern world: blood pressure, diabetes, and cholesterol. By listening, I had identified his "want" and now my answer was easy. I explained that these conditions need not be a lifelong sentence and proceeded to discuss his diet and lifestyle. It turns out one of his main sources of caloric intake was tortilla chips. I explained that if he could swap out the chips for some more nutrient dense foods, he could be on his way to getting rid of some of his medications . . . for life.

This story fills me with such joy because I heard something new in his voice after our discussion: hope. He said, "No one has talked to me about my diet, and maybe not needing medications." It was one of those experiences that keep me coming back to the job, despite the many frustrations. The beautiful thing was this solution came not from my "brilliant pharmacist brain" (which I definitely have), but from simply listening and responding.

If we can remember the importance of letting go of whatever else we may be thinking of on a particular moment, and instead key on to whoever is in front of us, we will find the magic answers will often appear with less effort.

Up to this point, I have alluded to listening intently to our patients. Equally important is listening to all members of our respective healthcare teams. Our teammates, when listened intently to, will help us arrive at the sometimes-elusive answers that evade us. Too often in healthcare, a single discipline or provider takes hold of a particular situation—often from the best of intentions—and they can get so wrapped up that they neglect to listen to those who work around them, leading to missed opportunities to problem solve. Just remember:

> ". . . but if you just listen to what's being said to you, and then react honestly, you generally get better results."

It's Not Just What Is Said, But How

Listening intently is not just about hearing what is said; it is also looking at nonverbal cues to observe how it is said.

For example, let's say there was a day when all my patients adhered to their medications, their blood sugars improved, and I got a bonus for being such a swell guy. When I get home, my wife asks me how my day was, and I say with a smile, "Great!" You can be fairly certain that my day was indeed great.

However, say my patients were rude, traffic sucked, and I found out that I had been overpaid and owed money back to my employer. When my wife asks how my day was, I instead snarl, throw my hands up in the air and yell, "Frikkin' fantastic!"

The power of visual cues are an important component to listening intently. Unfortunately, our current health-care system is not set up to encourage patient observation. Instead, it forces us to stare into computer screens, check boxes, and deal with a litany of alerts that *sometimes* relate to the patient who is sitting right in front of us. This book does not have a solution for our current Electronic Health Record woes per se, but I am here to remind us of the power and necessity of visual observation. While I don't have the power to revamp clunky, rage-inducing EHRs, I can remind you that *because* of the challenge it places on us, we must be even more focused using our visual observation.

This focus on *how* the words are said, not just the content, reminds me of a memorable patient I followed in our homeless clinic. These patients, as you might expect, required a unique set of care for their unique situations. I had been following him for his diabetes, which had been a challenge to manage as his blood sugar fluctuated so much. He was on multiple medications, including insulin, and his blood sugar would rise and fall precipitously because his food situation was always in flux. There were times where he had very little, or only sugary snacks, or there were donuts at our facility in which case . . . his blood sugar would go up even more.

However, things had calmed down for him, and his housing situation had become fairly stable, and his blood sugars followed. We were making real progress, and despite his reserved manner, I could see he was happier as his health issues were becoming better controlled. Another aspect that I admired in him was that despite his tough life circumstances, he was always in a jovial mood, had a smile on his face, and never seemed fazed by the difficulties of his reality.

At our next appointment, I greeted him, and we walked back to my office. He definitely seemed off despite saying that he was doing alright. He looked anxious, almost afraid to tell me something. When I pressed him for how his blood sugars had been doing, he dodged the question, and I realized something was up. It was how defeated he sounded when he talked that made me concerned.

I started to get the feeling that this appointment would not be about his blood sugar. I tried to continue on with the interview and asked him how his diet had been. This is when he finally admitted to me:

"I haven't eaten in four days."

They didn't teach me how to handle this in pharmacy school.

At first sight, I had known something was up, and finally, thanks to some repeated questioning, I was able to get to the root of the problem. By the end of the appointment, I had engaged our social worker and gotten the patient something to eat and resources in the community to continue to eat. Additionally, he had been kicked out of his transitional housing and had been without his medications for several days, so I was at least able to help get those refilled for him.

In the end, he wound up in a much better housing location that treated him better and had better food, and his mood as well as blood sugars improved. It was through the power of listening intently to both verbal and nonverbal cues that helped me arrive at the solution for this patient.

Thanks to my improv training and mindset, I was well practiced and ready for when this situation arose, and by working on listening intently yourself, you will find yourself ready for when the situation arises for you as well.

Chapter 7

TEAMWORK

How Improv Can Make the Dream Work

A pharmacist, a retired police officer, a college student, a garden director, a nurse practitioner, an academic administrator, and an entrepreneur walk onto a stage. This sentence looks like the beginning of a joke, and in a way, if you count the fact that it ends in laughter, you would not be far off. The description of this eclectic group is better known to me as "3rd Beats," and was Tucson's longest running improvised hip hop team.

It was one of the many improv teams I was a part of, as well as one of the most unique and diverse. Our group would likely not have been close outside of the walls of our improv theater, not because we wouldn't have gotten along, but because our paths wouldn't have crossed otherwise. Our ages ranged from sixteen to "sixty-ish," and we came from all over the country: Arizona, Pennsylvania, New York, and South Dakota. Yet this unlikely group of improvisers and friends was easily the most fun and successful improv group I have been privileged to perform with. As I mentioned, we would improvise rapping as part of our show and scene inspiration. Two of our team were excellent beatboxers, and so whenever a scene called for some hip-hop, one of them would drop a beat and off we would go.

What was our secret sauce? How were we so successful even though, in another life, we may have never crossed paths or become friends? The two words that helped us bond and find a shared goal are *group mind.*

Group mind is taking a population of people and finding a way to share a common vision or goal, whether on a team of improvised rappers, a football team on a mission to win a championship, or a multidisciplinary healthcare team working together with the common goal of taking care of patients. The most successful teams are the ones that have a clear goal in mind. When groups can find this focus, they can build something greater than the sum of their parts.

Improvisers are great at generating a clear vision and executing it by developing their group mind. The best teams that I have performed with all have this similar experience after a show. Inevitably, we end up recounting what went well and trying to ignore what went poorly. When recalling a great scene, one or two other improvers will chime in and say, "I had that exact same idea!" or, "I was going to start the scene the same way!" The teams that have developed their vision and then practiced repeatedly together have these "great minds think alike" moments during shows.

This sort of group mind doesn't just happen at once. Improv takes practice and rehearsal to develop a team's vision. Players understand each other's styles, favorite characters, and comfort zones, so that when a show is performed, the sum of the parts really ends up being greater than the whole.

This process of finding group mind helps to create fun and exciting improv shows, which is great if you are an improviser! However, you are more likely a healthcare worker, and you may be wondering what the deal is with healthcare and group mind.

Group mind doesn't often happen in healthcare.

Think about what the shared vision or goal should be: Put the patient first so that they are left in better health than before entering the healthcare system. The ultimate mission is to care for the patient.

Unfortunately, the mission can get distorted when there are actually many competing goals:

- generating revenue
- minimizing costs
- maximizing "billable or code-able" procedures
- interdepartmental rivalry
- interdisciplinary rivalry
- desire to be right
- avoidance of blame

Do any of these experiences sound familiar? Have you ever found yourself feeling like your organization or your team does not act in a way that's in the best interest of the patient? Or that you are not clear what your mission or goal is? Is your mission *really* to check boxes on a screen and follow rules, or is it to provide 100 percent of your attention to your patient?

In order to find more joy in our work in healthcare, while also providing the care that patients deserve, we need to work on our own healthcare version of "group mind." The lack of a clear vision and goal impede our ability to properly take care of patients.

Improv and Healthcare Ain't a One Person Show: How Improv and Healthcare Are Team Sports

The typical image of a "healthcare hero" is usually the lone soul cracking a tough diagnosis, cracking a chest open to massage a damaged heart, or cracking a dry joke after another exhausting day in the operating room. While this image gets views and clicks and drives an entire industry of barely believable medical dramas filled with impossibly attractive actors and actresses, it does not do justice to the true team nature of healthcare. Sure, the lone doctor may crack a diagnosis, but not without the X-ray tech getting a perfect image or the phlebotomist tirelessly drawing blood. And a cardiologist may massage a damaged heart back to health, but not without the staff keeping the operating room clean and sterile. Oh, and a surgeon doesn't crack a perfectly timed dry joke without a pharmacist probably telling a less funny joke earlier that inspired the more refined version. The point is, it takes more than a lone healthcare ranger to save the day. It takes a team.

Any group, whether it's the Chicago Cubs, a new business startup, or a primary care office, that is working toward a shared vision or goal is likely a team of some sort. Improv itself is a team sport. With some exceptions, improv shows consist of teams of multiple people. When I tell people I perform improv, they usually tell me a joke they heard that "would be good for my act," or they ask "how that standup thing" is going. Most of the time, I simply "yes, and" their small error by saying thanks for the material, and the standup is going great. I am not narcissistic enough to think that someone cares *that* much about the difference in improv versus standup and what it is I actually do in my spare time.

However, I am narcissistic enough to think that if you bought a book, written by me, filled with my experiences and thoughts, you may indeed care about the difference and how it relates to teamwork.

In the setting of a teamwork discussion, the main difference of improvisation and standup comedy is that standup is usually a one-person show. Improv, as I said, is generally a team sport.

What I love about improvisation is that it takes the entire group to be successful, especially when they have a great group mind working. Each member of the team has their own strength, personality, and background. These different backgrounds and strengths are what help a team thrive in a variety of scenes over time.

For a standup comedian, it is you, and you alone. There is no one there to help if you are bombing, struggling, or need help transitioning to a new joke. The strengths you have are the only strengths on that stage. I am not saying this is better or worse, just highlighting the differences.

Another important aspect of teamwork in improvisation is the ability to share the spotlight and energy. Within each scene, there will be different "moves" needed. Some are moves that bring big laughs. Others are moves that help set up those big laughs. Think of it like an alley-oop in basketball. Sure it is fun to watch someone slam it down, but someone has to throw that pass. Improv has no room for someone with a large ego that cannot share the "energy" of scenes. The energy of a scene is ever moving, and the spotlight must be able to shift quickly and smoothly. In this way, improv teaches us the importance of putting one's ego aside to serve the larger scene. Some of the most cringeworthy improv scenes are ones where either one person steals all the energy of a scene or the entire group refuses to bring any energy. They sit off on the side of the stage, or perform in a scene with hesitation and apprehension. Oftentimes, they think they are being polite by "letting someone else have a chance." However, it is important to read a scene to see if it needs some energy or dialogue, and then be willing to provide it. Individuals and teams can make the mistakes of either being too much of a "ballhog" or being too "nice."

Standup is . . . well, a lot of spotlight and energy on a single person telling jokes. There is no one there to set you up. You create your own set ups and punch lines. I have seen standup comedians struggle with improvisation because of their need to have the spotlight and energy, to be the center of attention. It is a rude shock to them and, most likely their ego, to be told to tone down their energy and try to make others look good.

In essence, an improviser takes pleasure in success of team rather than self. They put the needs of the team first, because improv cannot be successful unless the whole team succeeds.

Let's think about this in healthcare terms. When we are practicing, should it be a one person show, or is it a team event? Can one person carry a pharmacy/medicine team/ management team? Is it advisable to go this route?

The reality is that healthcare is a team sport. We need to remember we are working as a team in service of our patients. Healthcare cannot be successful unless the whole team succeeds. Healthcare and improv are team sports, and I think we have forgotten what "winning" means.

In healthcare, winning means that the patient gets better, and as a bonus, I think it should also mean that the provider and patient enjoy the experience as much as certain situations and diagnoses will allow. Unfortunately, winning oftentimes seems to mean that a particular specialty gets to do a procedure or one member of the team tries to carry the entire load to the point of burnout. If I haven't said it enough, I will reiterate that we work amongst some of the smartest and best-trained healthcare providers the world has ever known. Instead of thinking that it has to be surgery/cardiology/the dietician/the pharmacist/the RN that saves the day, let's sit back, share some energy, and lean on each other's expertise for solutions. This requires checking our ego and letting the patient guide us in our interactions. Some patients will feel more comfortable talking with a medical assistant rather than the doctor. Sometimes the solution will come from a social worker and not the surgeon. A pharmacy technician may catch an error a pharmacist misses. To this I say, "Great." In the end, it is not about the degrees or letters after our name that matter but that the right outcome is reached.

"Got Your Back"

The last thing our improv teams do before we step on stage is provide a simple reminder that we are there for each other on stage, that we have a common vision, and that we will support each other fearlessly.

The moment before we step on stage, we all go around to one another and give everyone a pat on the back, saying, "Got your back."

This simple, three-word phrase locks us in, reminds our egos to shut up for the next twenty minutes, and provides clarity as to what "winning" will look like on stage. Improvisers must be able to support each other, otherwise the team will fail, the audience will not laugh, and tears will fall. On an individual level, it always feels good to know that someone is looking out for you. Nobody likes feeling isolated, and if you have ever found yourself in a scene, not knowing what the next thing to do or say is, you can feel like the loneliest person on the planet. When we have the support of each other, we are less afraid to take risks, to be bold on stage, and know someone will be there to help pick us up if we falter.

"Got your back" symbolizes the community of support that is fostered on an improv team. As I mentioned before, there is no room for ego. There is also no room for tearing each other down, belittling, or generally making people feel like shit for what they did on stage. Improvisation can be a scary undertaking, and the goal of the team is to support each other, rather than tearing one another down. It's this community of support that allows teams to grow together, become better cohesive units, and ultimately generate that group mind I have talked so much about.

Contrast this improv community of support to what we face in healthcare. I will discuss later in the book about how new ideas and curiosity are often snuffed out in favor of the status quo, but it certainly feels like there is often an "eat the young" hierarchy in healthcare. How are healthcare teams supposed to work toward the goal of caring for patients if we spend our energy tearing down our colleagues, other professions, and organizations? The answer is we won't. And we certainly haven't.

On a daily basis, we need to remind those we work with that we "have their back." I am a personal-space nut, so I keep my distance from others. My time on New York City subways is about as nightmarish as it gets for me, so I will not physically tap someone's back. However, I make a point of saying, "I got your back," if someone is having a rough day, if someone expresses appreciation for help I gave them, or if I just feel like it. This expression is likely not a silver bullet for our divisive healthcare system, but it can be a simple, easy, and effective way to make your teammates feel appreciated and supported.

I mentioned the feeling of being alone on stage when you don't know what to do or what the next move should be and that having a great team who has got your back helps to alleviate that nerve-wracking feeling. That feeling of loneliness can also manifest itself in healthcare, and I think that we have done a poor job of creating a culture that helps to support those of us when we do feel alone.

This loneliness can be manifested in multiple ways. There is the literal "only person on the shift" loneliness that is inevitable given certain environments. (Looking at you, graveyard-shift pharmacists. Glad you can handle it, because I am certainly not cut out for that work.) While there isn't a physical team there to help pick you up on those lonely nights, your organization can "have your back" and support you by providing the right tools for success. This can be properly training and preparing you for your tasks. It could be having the right supporting technology and resources to get you through not having a physical team there to assist. Or this could mean that our hypothetical lonesome practitioner develops relationships with other disciplines, and they get through the dark, lonely night together.

Of course, this is for the literal lonely feeling. There are other times when it feels like you are on an island, all alone, despite being surrounded by your colleagues. The key difference is if those colleagues around you support you, tear you down, or remain indifferent. With the pace at which we are expected to work, and the high expectations placed on us, it is too easy to fall into the trap of letting our stress get in the way of supporting those we work with. This could be a new trainee on their first day who is asking the "same dumb questions" that each new trainee asks every month they rotate through. In this case, often indifference and an attitude of "everyone else had to figure it out for themselves" takes over, and precious hours and days are wasted because this new person wasn't supported.

Another example is when someone brings up a problem, question, or "outside the box" idea, and the questioner is actively ridiculed because our attachment to the status quo is so strong in healthcare. If all our patients were perfectly healthy, our system made no errors that harmed patients, and every patient was left vastly improved, this would be a valid reaction. However, our outcomes are a far cry from that utopia. The significance of this is that "got your back" should apply to those who raise questions, concerns, or new ideas. The alternative is an unchanging healthcare system that is failing its providers and patients.

Improv is successful because it is built around a culture of support, teamwork, and "got your back-edness." Its participants are less afraid to take risks, make mistakes, and innovate. This supportive culture is what attracted me to improv, and as a healthcare provider, provided such a stark contrast. What we need to apply in healthcare is an attitude of group mind, working toward the common goal of making our patients healthier, while supporting each other in the process. By applying this attitude, our healthcare providers will feel supported and never feel like they are "alone on stage."

Chapter 8

GO DEEPER, NOT WIDER

Because When Everything's a Priority, Nothing's a Priority

Going on a vacation is usually a welcome getaway from the stresses of everyday life. You can leave your worries and cares behind. If you have kids (and some nice grandparents), you can leave those behind too. Vacations are a great way to relax, slow down, and forget about your cares.

Does this sound like one of your vacations? If not, let me paint an alternate scenario:

You plan your itinerary down to the minute. You cannot waste a moment of your precious personal time off, so every bit of your non-work responsibilities must be savored to the *max*. Sure, that connecting flight is going to be a *little* tight, but you couldn't beat that deal you found. Life is all about *optimization*, baby, and you are optimizing this vacation to the *max*. Once you arrive at your destination, there are five minutes built into the schedule to get unpacked before your nonstop-five-days-of-full-on-fun-and-activities can begin! Life is too short not to try everything there is to do while you are visiting this new place, so you bounce from meal to activity to meal to excursion to snack to historic walk downtown to meal to . . . *the max* of exhaustion. You might find yourself saying, at the end of your vacation, "I need a vacation to recover from my vacation."

In scenario two, you spread yourself too thin, try to do too much, and end up not enjoying much of anything. This "do it all" approach leaves you burnt out and not enjoying any one thing. I see it happen often in healthcare where a wide variety of responsibilities are expected to fit into an unrealistic timeframe. Like an overdone vacation, nothing great is enjoyed or accomplished. How can we turn this source of frustration around?

The answer I have learned as an improviser is to go deeper, not wider.

"Build skyscrapers, not subdivisions." This is the advice of my improv teacher and dear friend, Justin Lukasewicz, who described the improv concept of "go deeper not wider." The goal of an improv scene is obviously to be funny. More specifically, it is to find a single funny or interesting concept or "game" of the scene and explore it in depth. Ideally, in the first few lines improvisers will identify the game of the scene, and "heighten" or increase the comedic value by highlighting that single funny or interesting thing in a scene. Everything that happens in a successful improv scene will be in service of that interesting thing.

The opposite of that is to go "wider." Going wider in an improv scene happens when the improvisers bring lots of new and different "games" or ideas into the scene. Oftentimes, this will happen with newer improvisers who aren't as adept at finding the game, and so they will, as we say, start "inventing" different "funny" or interesting concepts. Instead of focusing on a single funny or interesting "game," they will bring multiple games in without ever exploring any one thing in great detail. These types of scenes tend to be more frenetic, disjointed, and unfunny. In this scenario, the players are like that family trying to do everything on vacation; there is a lot of energy and jumping around, but by the end, nobody has really had a good time.

This concept of "deeper not wider" is well known to improvisers, although not always well practiced. It parallels the experience in healthcare where the motto seems like "everything is a priority." Well, if everything is a priority, nothing is a priority. Here is how going "wider not deeper" feels like from a community pharmacist's perspective. Here are their priorities and tasks:

- checking prescription accuracy
- vaccinations
- drive-thru window questions
- counseling at the pharmacy counter
- phone call to insurance company
- phone call to doctor's office
- bathroom breaks
- lunch breaks

To my community pharmacist friends, I apologize for missing anything, but you get the point. This scenario will parallel any other profession as well: there is so much asked of us that it is nearly impossible to be good at any single thing.

From a healthcare organizational and management standpoint, there are too many points of emphasis so no particular initiative can get enough time or monetary resources to make a real difference. At any time, the priority could be preventing infection, reducing medical errors, preparing for a visit from an accrediting body, implementing telehealth, streamlining appointment scheduling, helping opioid reduction, providing diabetes management, coordinating third party contracts . . . and the list can go on indefinitely. Like I said, when everything is a priority, nothing is a priority. I can proudly say that many a "this is a new focus" email to me has gone directly to the trash bin. I am too busy focusing on my actual priority, which is taking care of patients directly. Lost in the shuffle of all of these "great, new ideas" is the actual care and experience of the patients.

You may be reading this saying, "Hold on Dr. 'Yes, And,' I thought the whole idea of improv and the 'yes, and' philosophy was that we didn't say no to new ideas . . . ya hypocrite." Well, you got me—sort of. We still can say yes to an idea, but it doesn't mean we have to implement it right away. With improv training, there is a progression of applying "yes, and" to get the best comedy possible. When an improviser first starts, it is simply about overcoming your fear of making up comedy, learning to say yes, and giving 100 percent of your energy to whatever choice was made in a scene. My analogy is walking down a hotel hallway, and the only goal is to pick a door, any door, and kick it in with all of your energy and focus. However, as one progresses and becomes more experienced, you learn to make "yes, and" choices that are stronger comedically. The hotel hallway analogy continues, but the goal becomes to pick the *right* door to follow with all your energy.

We simply live in a world of limited time, money, and other resources. Our goal in healthcare shouldn't be to branch out and "build subdivisions" because a truly great idea may never get the attention it deserves to make a difference. The key is to identify the markers of health that have the biggest impact and cost both monetarily and on a human level and put most of your energy (go deeper) into solving those problems. The ability to choose the most impactful interventions to get the biggest return falls into the Pareto Principle, or "80/20 Rule," which says that 80 percent of your outcome comes from 20 percent of your input. In essence, by applying this rule, we aim to find an intervention that is conceivably simple and requires a small amount of resources that provides a large return on investment. One place I have seen this is in my patients who have uncontrolled diabetes who are drinking a large volume of sugary soda a day. By simply removing this single offending food item, their blood sugar can improve dramatically and have a drastic impact on their overall health.

This principle applies universally—anything from advertising to a health intervention. With so many competing priorities in healthcare, I don't think we even get a chance to apply the 20 percent needed to tackle our biggest problems. We are simply spread too thin.

As this book is being written, we are in the middle of the COVID-19 pandemic. We have seen a sudden and massive shift in our healthcare resources and utilization. It seems all guns are trained on everything COVID-19. On the one hand, it is an example of going deeper on a particular problem. On the other hand, within its handling, resources and focus are massively spread out on different priorities such as social distancing, quarantines, and delaying elective procedures, to name a few.

The news is not all bad on the COVID-19 response front, however. In a valiant and, in my opinion, well-guided effort to prevent hospital and other healthcare facilities from being places of high exposure, a seemingly overnight revolution in telemedicine has taken place. I count myself lucky to be in the group that has been a part of this new method of delivering healthcare remotely. As both an observer and a participant, I can say that there was a focused and directed push to move outpatient appointments to virtual. In short order, the technology, legislation, and procedures have been put in place to try to assure patients are getting as good of care as possible away from the physical clinic space. For a short period of time, a specific goal was identified, and a huge focus was put on its implementation. The result was surprising to a skeptic like me: a relatively smooth transition and a high level of satisfaction for both the providers and the patients.

The point made in this example is that while it seems so many of our problems in healthcare are insurmountable, the reality is it just takes the focus and priority of going really deep and solving that problem. Our healthcare system constantly applies Band-Aids to a wide range of problems, but we should have the courage to pick one or two and put the majority of our resources into solving that problem.

Before I move on to the individual approach to going deeper not wider, I would be remiss if didn't address the possibility that it seems like I am trying to dismiss smaller problems in healthcare (I am a poet and didn't even know it). It may seem like I am sounding cruel in the realm of only focusing on a few "big problems" in healthcare and thus excluding those with more rare conditions or issues. I want to make sure I do not come off in that way with my "deeper not wider" approach. We have an ethical duty to treat all persons with all types of conditions, no matter how common or rare. My lament at a "wider not deeper" approach from a macro level in healthcare is more from a perspective of frustration at the competing priorities of organizational oversight, administrative burdens, and an increase in the breadth of tasks that are asked of us that may provide limited utility or improvement in outcomes. The challenge at the high level of healthcare is to find a way to streamline all of the competing priorities so that in a world of limited resources, we get the biggest bang for our buck while leaving resources available for those issues and problems that are less common, but are still important to address.

Going Deeper, Not Wider: An Individual Approach

Up to this point, I have examined what the improv tenet of going deeper not wider could mean on a larger scale in healthcare. This attitude of trying to do too much makes its way down to an individual healthcare provider level also. Trying to go "deeper not wider" is nearly impossible within an individual patient encounter. There are myriad alerts: the address, reminders to click on or off, and "boxes to check" just to get to the point of taking care of the actual patient's concerns. I could make the argument that all of these do help to establish a "base reality" and that this tenet is an important one for improv and healthcare. However, in its execution, it leaves healthcare providers spread over a competing number of priorities, leaving less time to focus in on patient concerns. And about those patient concerns. Let's not forget another priority is to get the appointment over with as soon as possible, so there is a time crunch as well. With the average primary care appointment lasting only seventeen minutes and people being more sick than ever, there is no time to address any single issue with any depth.[20]

The issue with having so little time and so many problems in a patient appointment should be obvious: there is entirely too much breadth to cover, and even if we could pick one or two areas of focus, there is not enough time to explore the issue in any detail. The end result is that "on

---

20. Ming Tai-Seale, Thomas G. McGuire, and Weimin Zhang, "Time Allocation in Primary Care Office Visits," *Health Services Research* 42, no. 5 (October 2007): 1871–94, https://www.ncbi.nlm.nih.gov/pmc/articles/PMC2254573/.

paper" we have checked our boxes and have done a "good job" according to third party payers and office managers. In reality, we have patients that leave without being able to fully address their concerns, who have problems that cannot be worked on, and there is certainly no time for an exploration into the root cause of problem. Too often, patients leave their appointment with concerns still on their mind, questions unanswered, and a rushed prescription for another medication that completely neglects to address the root of whatever problem it is they are having. Next, we are going to see that despite the many challenges in healthcare, there are ways to overcome them to deliver great care for our patients.

Thrive in Your Healthcare Reality

In our healthcare system, we have to deal with certain realities, such as number and length of appointments, third party reimbursement, and large patient panels. In "healthcare utopia," we would get smaller patient loads and more time with each individual patient, and insurers would realize the value in "going deep" on the root cause of problems. Until then, we are going to have to (nay, get to) improvise and find a way to overcome the obstacles in the service of those we care for.

There is good news for you though! You are reading this improv book! Many of the topics that we have covered will help sharpen the tools in your tool belt to go "deeper not wider." My goal for you is to know how to quickly connect with your patients, and go as deep as you can in the time you have. By finding the most impactful problem or concern to focus on, you will be applying the Pareto Principle wherein putting less total spread-out effort will yield a greater gain for the patient.

So how will you be able to go "deeper" with your patients and stay within the confines of your practice? Let's do a quick recap of the other improv skills that we've built to improve your chance of success!

First, I have lost count of the number of times "yes, and" has been typed, but it's a lot, because it's important. If you are looking for a way to improve your patient encounter, it's probably because you are feeling constrained. So, first be willing to "yes, and" your frustration! Agree to the premise you are working with limits you'd rather not be dealing with. Every ounce of energy you spend worrying about what you can't control is energy that won't be spent on the sparse time you have with the patient.

When you see the patient, apply the "yes, and" philosophy to them. Agree to listen to what seems to be their most significant problem, and do your best to identify and address it. If you spend the appointment arguing, saying no, and disagreeing, the chances of successfully communicating is low.

Speaking of communication, remember to communicate clearly and specifically! Make sure to communicate your "base reality" at the top of the interview: who you are, what your goal is as a provider for that appointment, and why you think that is important. Getting the information out at the top of the appointment will save a lot of time backtracking and re-explaining. Also, don't be shy in sharing what your time limit is. I know that I have gone past appointment times when I thought that the specific patient and situation warranted it, but providing the expectation that "we have fifteen minutes to talk about your blood sugars" can help focus the patient and help them realize there is less time for getting off topic. Informing them of the time expectation of the appointment can also serve as a reminder for yourself. I know that I have been guilty of going too long because the allotted time just slipped my mind as I was engaged in the appointment.

Be sure to listen intently. This is not step three—this is a step that should be done throughout the appointment. Applying the idea of listening intently, remembering both verbal and nonverbal clues, will help you identify the patient's primary concern/want/why of that appointment. It will provide you the information to go deeper into a few problems to hopefully get the greatest impact for the intervention.

Apply group mind by having a shared vision and goal. Once you introduce yourself and your goals for the appointment, listen intently to what the patient is concerned about. And then, find a shared goal for the appointment. Also, lean on your team! Many times, before walking into a patient's room, some golden words of warning saved me from saying the wrong word or touching on a subject the patient was not in the mood to discuss. Lean on each other's expertise as well. If you realize that a patient has a concern that is outside your scope or area of expertise, don't be afraid to table that problem and get another provider who would be better suited to address it. This doesn't mean you have to ignore a patient's concern, but be honest and say you don't know, and don't want to give them information that could do more harm than good. Offer to have them follow up with someone who has more expertise. As I mentioned above, lean on each other's expertise.

Finally, remember what winning looks like: it means the patient's health should improve because of the interventions made at the appointment. By focusing on the most important issues despite limited time, you will be able to have the greatest impact by going as deep as possible on what matters.

Chapter 9

GET OUT OF YOUR HEAD AND JUST GO

Since When Has Overthinking Ever Really Helped?

Just Go Already

Quick! Give me a two-minute speech about how you would make healthcare an enjoyable experience for patients and providers! No waiting! Let's hear it. Also, give it in an Australian accent, mate!

Alright, too difficult? Let's try this exercise again.

Quick! Give me a two-minute speech about your favorite vacation destination. Hurry, no time to plan! Just start. Also, give it in an Australian accent, mate. Bonus points if your favorite destination is Australia!

Did you pass the "quick improvised speech" test? Were you able to jump right in and start making your points, confidently, without pausing? Or, did you sit there, in your head, and ponder the best way to introduce this hypothetical speech to no one in particular, debating the merits of the arguments, eventually giving up before even starting?

If you found yourself part of the second scenario, don't feel too bad. It is not instinctual to jump into a speech without prepared points or preparation. However, it is also not uncommon, especially for us overanalyzers that tend to find ourselves working in healthcare, to get our ideas halted with a dose of overthinking. There is nothing wrong with thinking through a problem or idea, but it's when we sit and overthink a problem or idea that no progress is made. The paralysis by analysis pretty much sums up my dating life in high school . . . and college . . . and early adulthood.

In healthcare, we are trained to have a precise solution to a problem. Patient problems are complex, and the system we work in is as complicated as ever—just try and get an explanation about your "explanation of benefits"! We have been trained to *really think* through possible solutions, analyzing all the data available, to come to our best solution. This deep approach works great when we have an indefinite amount of time to spend on a problem, an indefinite amount of data to base our decision on, and an indefinite amount of resources to pay us while we pontificate.

Our reality is much different. We rarely have the full picture of a problem, there is almost always a deadline, and there is a finite amount of resources available for our compensation. So how are we, those of analytical and risk-averse minds, supposed to solve our most complex problems?

Just go.

One of the most successful and well-known improvisers is Amy Poehler. She has a quote that perfectly sums up the idea of avoiding the "paralysis by analysis" and simply going. She says in regards to an improv scene:

> "Don't start a scene where two people are talking about jumping out of a plane. Start the scene having already jumped."[21]

As an improviser, this has taught me the importance of starting right at the interesting or fun part of a scene. By starting a scene "in the middle," we remove the fluff and boring prelude. An improv show, like trying to solve a pressing problem in healthcare, has a finite amount of time. With both, we cannot waste too much time getting to the important parts. The difference between the two is that improv teaches us how to cut right to the important parts while it seems that too much time is wasted in healthcare *talking around* the problem before addressing it directly.

When trying to innovate, create ideas, or tackle problems, we often encounter some form of "writer's block." Whether it's an inability to think of the next word to say, being unsure of the next step to take, or being stuck in "overthinking" mode, the result is the same: no progress. I have felt the need to get things just right before even truly starting the project, whether it's starting a project at work or trying to start a business.

21. Amy Poehler, "Take Your Risk NOW," Harvard University's 2011 Class Day speech, Tercentenary Theater in Harvard Yard, 25 May 2011, https://www.english speecheschannel.com/english-speeches/amy-poehler-speech/.

As someone who works in healthcare, we are conditioned that we must have all the data, all the trials, and all the analysis before trying something new. It comes from a place of safety, which is commendable and important. The downside is that it feels like there must be too many "ducks in a row" needed before exploring something new or different. The reality is that we do work under conditions of uncertainty and these are inherent in our chosen profession, but we're not thriving in it as much as we could be. Some of us do well with *just enough* information, yet it seems like a large portion of providers and those in healthcare will wait until they have *all* the data. That point, for most problems, is unlikely to come quickly enough, and we must learn to get comfortable making adjustments and changes with a reasonable amount of information. Otherwise, nothing will improve because nothing will change.

Essentially, what we are fighting against in healthcare is inertia. It's this big, daunting, "an object in motion remains in motion unless acted on by an outside force" energy that discourages so many from innovating or trying to implement a new idea. We are afraid to be that outside force. We think it takes too much force to make a change or make a difference.

There is not this sort of resistance in the world of improvisation. Remember, we jump out of airplanes and figure it out on the way down. However, I cannot condone actually jumping out of an airplane before thinking about a parachute (although, according an article in the British Medical Journal, parachutes do not prevent death or major trauma when jumping out of an aircraft[22]). It is this "motion" of creation that helps fuel comedy at the famed Second City in Chicago. Their cast uses improvisation to brainstorm ideas for their comedy sketches, and *then* sifts out and refines them. Instead of sitting around, trying to "think of the best ideas" they just start *going*.

While we don't want to improvise a complex surgery or a new medication, we can apply the brainstorming process of just "going" without judgment or overthought. Turning off our judgment is one of the weapons that improv provides us. How many times have you had an idea that you were excited about? This idea that could save lives? That could change how we practice? Yet, before you brought your idea to your boss or even a friend, your judgment brain convinced you that it was stupid. Or maybe it wasn't realistic. Or there was just too much in the way to make it a reality. We'll talk later about improv and overcoming limiting beliefs, but applying the improv mindset to ideas and innovation helps to turn off this judgment.

This mindset of "just go" to foster innovation is crucial for organizations as well. By saying "yes, and" to new and different ideas, healthcare organizations can be the breeding ground for innovation. Of course, this must be accomplished by creating a culture that embraces employees who bring new ideas and are at least willing to move forward with considering them. The alternative is an environment

---

22. Robert W. Yeh, et al, "Look Before You Leap: Parachute use to prevent death and major trauma when jumping from aircraft: randomized controlled trial," *BMJ* 2018, 363 (13 December 2018), https://www.bmj.com/content/363/bmj.k5094.

that will stifle employee creativity, lead to burnout, and ultimately leave innovation dead in the water.

Just *go*. Remember, these are just ideas. They are not being implemented. They are not policy. No patients can be harmed by an idea. Remember that phrase, "yes, and"? Say yes to where your mind wants to go with an idea. Explore it, go deeper not wider. This is not a time for perfection. Too many ideas are snuffed out because we let "perfect be the enemy of good." As famed General George S. Patton said, "A good plan, violently executed now, is better than a perfect plan next week." Who knew "Old Blood and Guts" had an improv mindset?

Make More Statements, Ask Fewer Questions

I realize that I ironically ended my last section with a question, as we now transition into a section on asking fewer questions. Am I sorry? Yes. Will I make the same mistake again? Well, it's happening as I type. Let's move on before I ask more questions, shall we? Aw shucks.

As you can see, it's easy to get caught in a question loop, and not move a conversation, or book, forward. A better way to move forward is, instead of asking endless questions, just go, make a bold statement then listen and respond to the reaction.

To drive the point home of how questions can often not help us make progress or find clarity, imagine you are

CHAPTER 9: GET OUT OF YOUR HEAD AND JUST GO

sitting in a crowd at an improv comedy show. You are ready for a laugh after a long week. The first improv group takes the stage, the energy in the theater is electric, and the show begins with the following lines:

"Who are you?"

"What's going on here?"

Depending on your level of adult beverage consumption or existential self-reflection, you are definitely asking question two, and maybe circling back to question one. These questions have left you with more questions than answers to start the show.

While this scene didn't happen in a show, it is a real example. I still remember these two aspiring improvisers at an audition at our company. They had been through several levels of our classes, shown a deep commitment to learning the craft, and an inspiring enthusiasm for wanting to be a part of our improv company. Yet, in their first scene at the audition, they had broken one of the cardinal rules of improvisation:

Don't ask questions.

"Don't ask questions?" you are asking, ironically. "But how can a conversation or scene happen when you don't ask questions? How can you find out what is going on or needs to happen?"

Boy, you are really hanging on tightly to this question asking thing, but I'll fill you in on why questions are generally a no-fly zone on an improv stage. When I ask a question, I am not adding any new information to a scene. Question asking, while it seems like a "nice" thing to do, is actually one of the rudest things an improviser can do. When I ask you a hypothetical improviser a question, what I am actually doing is putting all of the work on you to create something. You now have to create all of the information out of thin air. Let's see an example of how question asking makes moving forward in an improv scene a challenge and a burden for the person being asked the question:

Person 1: We should go out for dinner tonight.

Person 2: Where should we go?

Person 1 now has to think of what they want, where they want to go, and thus the scene will slow down and not move forward as quickly. Let's see it played out a different way:

Person 1: We should go out for dinner tonight.

Person 2: Yes, and we're getting tacos, end of story.

Person 1: You always pick where we go, and I think we should get pizza.

In this second scenario, "Person 1" had a statement to react to versus trying to create an entire attitude, location, and "want" for where to go eat. As I have discussed previously, all of the answers we need in a conversation are right in front of us if we are able to simply listen and react.

Of course, "real life" is not "improv life," and I don't expect questions to never happen. Heck, I have used the device of asking questions several times in this book alone. How do you think that's working?

While I am not advocating that we never ask questions of our patients or our team members, I am making the argument that focusing on making statements helps to break the kinetic energy if we are experiencing some kind of writer's block or brainstorming block. In improv scenes, making statements helps to garner a reaction and move the scene forward. When trying to troubleshoot a problem, develop a new policy, or even work with a patient, making a statement may help to break the stalemate you are facing.

This is a book about applying improv to healthcare, but let me provide another example of the "say statements and not questions" approach that I have applied often in the real world with success. Now, pardon as I ask a hypothetical *question* to set the stage, and feel free to call me a hypocrite. Have you ever found yourself among a large group of friends and you decide to order pizza? First, congratulations on at least selecting a type of food. Too often the debate roars at *what* should be ordered to eat. If you found yourself at "pizza," you are well ahead of our hypothetical curve.

The next questions to come up are inevitably, "Where should we order from?" and "What kind of pizza should we get?" The correct answer is sausage and onions, but let's continue with our hypothetical. We live in a world with an absurd amount of pizza options. We are inundated with pizza places, types, and toppings. If you are like me, your group of friends is generally polite and says, "I don't care.

What do *you guys* want?" This act of kindness usually starts an avalanche of politeness, with everyone in the group deferring to each other to make a choice. Unfortunately, thirty minutes later, when your piping hot pizza should be being delivered, your group is still deliberating as to who should decide where and what kind of pizza to have delivered. By this point, your group is hungry, and is getting hangrier by the moment. Maybe it ends with someone yelling, "I don't even like pizza! Why don't we get Mexican food?" at which point the kindness cycle begins, and you are no closer to your original food destination.

I used to fall victim to this endless cycle of kindness and hunger. It was frustrating being around seemingly intelligent people who just couldn't move forward and make a choice about something so inconsequential as dinner. Then I started applying the improv mindset of "statements not questions." What happened was, relatively speaking, miraculous: groups were able to move forward, find a consensus, and order food with relative ease and speed!

Here is how a scenario would go, after consensus reached for pizza:

Someone from group: "What should we get?"

Someone else from group: "I don't really care, you guys get what you want."

Me, sensing the situation derailing quickly: "Let's order from Bianci's. We should get one supreme with everything on it, one pepperoni, and one veggie.

Also, no breadsticks. They are a waste. It's just pizza without any of the good shit on it."

The reaction was basically either "that sounds good," or "I don't like any of those things," from one or two people. At this point, a quick tweak to one of our pizza selections was made, the order was placed, and just as the group was about to hit the "hangry" phase, our piping-hot pizzas would show up to save the day (although the true hero here was me, if I do say so myself).

Moving forward and generating ideas works best when we make statements instead of stewing in questions. I know I have taken you around the world of improvisation to pizza delivery, but beyond making decisive dinnertime decisions, making statements is useful for driving decisions in health-care. For example, when a medicine or primary care team is considering the best course of action on a complex patient. I have been in situations where the question, "Well, what do we want to do?" is asked and is responded to with a chorus of crickets. However, in similar situations, sometimes a statement of an idea, even not the best idea, can stimulate further conversation and an even better course of action. Healthcare education, by its design, is filled with questions for trainees; from tests to internships they are questioned regularly. However, some of the most effective learning I have had with my students and residents is when they give me a statement of a plan that is incorrect. Rather than ask, "What do you think the answer is?" I will tell them to give me the best plan they have, or if I am feeling gener-ous, give them two options and tell them to pick one and explain why. Even when they are "wrong," they get a chance for constructive feedback and deeper learning. I have seen some of the biggest "aha" moments from trainees when they make an incorrect statement and then absorb the reasons why it was incorrect.

Just making an idea statement, even if it is not the best, or remotely what the final product or plan will look like, is more effective than sitting in our heads, overthinking and questioning. A statement will generate opinions and other ideas from others you work with. It will stimulate conversation. Statements give us something to react to and be inspired by. They help break the stalemate of overthinking and inactivity.

So, when facing a tough problem, a case of writer's block, a brainstorming session that just won't "storm," or indecision about what to get for lunch, remember not to get mired in an endless round of questions and overthinking. Instead, "Just *go*." Give a statement. The reactions and thoughts from others will provide the inspiration needed to get moving on a solution.

Make No Mistake:
There Are No "Real" Mistakes

One hang-up to the concept of "just go," especially in healthcare, is the fear of making mistakes. This hang-up is perfectly reasonable given the high stakes involved, but it often is this fear of mistakes that keeps knowledge from progressing and innovation from occurring. To help ease your, the reader's, mind about making a mistake in healthcare, how about this?

Confession time: I have made at least one known mistake in my career. It is embarrassing, and fortunately, it was caught by the patient before any harm could occur. The incident occurred back when I was doing a lot of order processing, and speed was the name of the game. I was quite good at quickly and safely verifying prescriptions and was being as "careful" as I thought I should be.

The patient, however, caught the error in question when *she* received a bottle of sildenafil, that little blue pill for erectile dysfunction. She knew better than to take it as she had no erection that was dysfunctional. Looking back, it was not a *hard* error to miss, as gender would have disqualified that patient for sildenafil immediately. It was clear I had made quite a *boner*. I clearly needed to *erect* a better way of avoiding errors.

Whew! Okay, now that I got all those sildenafil-related puns out of the way . . .

I was embarrassed by the mistake. Fortunately, my boss was quite forgiving and understanding of the situation. She is not a trained improviser, but she sure plays the part sometimes with her "yes, and" attitude! I recall her calling me into her office and saying that I had made an error, but fortunately the patient was not harmed, and they contacted us right away out of concern. Another thing my boss did was show understanding as to how such an error could have occurred. She acknowledged that in my job, I processed tens of thousands of prescriptions a year. As such, statistically, errors are inevitable. She also expressed that this was not the first time that particular provider had made an error ordering a prescription. In the end, she took the wind out of the sails of an event that could have been much more serious and dire and put me at ease, making it more learning opportunity than punitive situation.

Her goal in telling me was to *teach* me by showing me a mistake and offering suggestions to avoid future errors. It was not a moment to rub it in my face or make me feel any more worse than I already did. The actions she took in being understanding, empathetic, and patient helped me become a better pharmacist that day. Had she yelled, screamed, and berated me for an error that, although it was my fault, was not done out of incompetence, distraction, or malice, it would have had a number of deleterious effects:

1. I would not have felt comfortable coming to her if I made a future error.
2. I would have lost trust in her leadership.
3. I would have lost confidence in my abilities.
4. I would not want to work in such a hostile and anxiety-inducing culture.

Perhaps, most importantly:

5. I would not have learned from my mistake, and I would have been more likely to repeat it.

By addressing my error, and without knowing it, my manager was employing one of the most welcome and needed improv tenets in relation to healthcare: there are no real mistakes.[23]

You may be surprised to learn, if you haven't been paying attention to this book, that improv shows are unscripted. No improviser gets onto a stage and knows what they are going to be saying, singing, or doing during their set. There are, quite simply, no scripts. However, as would often happen when teaching one of my improv students or coaching a team, we would be rehearsing when, in the middle of a scene, an improviser would stop and say something along the lines of, "Oh, I messed that up." Sometimes this admission of "guilt" would come after a scene or show when breaking down a scene and be along the lines of, "I shouldn't have said that. I should have done something else."

My way of addressing this type of concern was usually sarcastic and an attempt at humor. I am in the comedy business after all. I would ask them, "Did the audience know you went off script?" Their response was usually delayed, and a little confused. "We don't have scripts."

Exactly.

If I am performing an improv scene, whatever I say *is* the script. There is no way I can deviate from it. Sure, I can "break" the improv rules by being a poor listener or just ignoring my scene partner. But the beautiful truth about improvisation is that you can never "mess up your lines." In fact, ironically as a pharmacist and improviser, I have really grown to detest "scripts," both of the preset lines and shorthand for prescription.

---

23. Yes, there are medication and other errors we must deal with appropriately, but the spirit is one without blame that seeks to find a solution.

The best improvisers realize that there are no mistakes on an improv stage. Instead, there are only opportunities. If an improviser sneezes, falls down, or has an otherwise embarrassing moment, they or their teammates can take that possible pitfall and turn it into a golden comedic moment. If you can recall from earlier in the book, my story about the incoherent screaming and dancing that Mishell turned into "the best hype man ever" is a perfect example of turning a "problem" into a gift. I'll give you another example. Our improv theater plays a rapping game called "Beastie Rap" that is essentially a call and response. One improviser sets a rhyme up and the other two attempts to complete it based on the setup. It is good clean fun. That is, unless an audience member insists on a word that rhymes with one of those four-letter "no no's" like, say, *duck*, which is what happened during a show I was hosting. The "suggestor" had had a few adult beverages and was attempting to show his friends how funny and clever he was. I took it as a challenge, and our improvisers started rhyming everything else with "duck" but the word that starts with the letter "f." After several rounds, they just ran out of words, without hitting the "f" word. To wrap it up, I said "Well, I think we got every word that rhymes with 'duck.' Let's give a round of applause for that guy's suggestion, I assume you are satisfied?" He had a good laugh, along with the audience. Instead of making the situation uncomfortable, I turned it into a gift for the audience and our improvisers.

A "mistake" in improvisation is often seized and turned into a comedic opportunity. The mistake becomes a fun new challenge, a chance for further comedy, an opportunity to support your teammates, and oftentimes a lesson as well. Contrasted with the world of healthcare, where mistakes, without denying their seriousness, are often followed by shame, punitive action, and no better understanding of their root cause. I have worked with lots of doctors, nurses, and pharmacists, and not one of them has ever expressed or shown a desire to purposely cause harm. We generally are a group of people who want to help others achieve better health outcomes. Along the way, given the complex health system we work in, mistakes are going to happen despite our best efforts. How we deal with those mistakes is the issue.

I think we need to take an improv mindset when it comes to mistakes in healthcare by turning them from taboo issues to opportunities to learn from. Ideally, we wouldn't make the same mistake again. The first step after a mistake is always to take care of the patient. Whether that means treatment to mitigate the physical or psychological effects of the mistake, make sure this occurs. Even in this first step, there is an opportunity. Improv comedy is based on reality and truth. In fact, there is less chance of litigation when errors are disclosed honestly.[24]

Once the patient is taken care of in regards to this mistake, it is then time to learn from it. When I made my sildenafil error, my manager was very good about being honest with me, providing the facts, and offering up solutions. For me, it was simple. Makes sure to check the gender when

---

24. Sandra G. Boodman, "Should hospitals—and doctors—apologize for medical mistakes?" *The Washington Post: Health & Science*, 12 March 2017, https://www .washingtonpost.com/national/health-science/should-hospitals--and-doctors- -apolgize-for-medical-mistakes/2017/03/10/1cad035a-fd20-11e6-8f41-ea6 ed597e4ca_story.html.

verifying sildenafil. That's the improv approach healthcare needs to take with errors: looking for solutions instead of looking for someone to blame.

The downside to focusing on blame and shame is that those involved aren't going to be open and comfortable discussing what may have gone wrong, and they will be silent about future errors. In fact, it's reported that most medical errors and mistakes go unreported. One article reports that for every medical error that causes injury to a patient, there may be one hundred errors or more that go unreported or undetected.[25] A culture that doesn't embrace errors is one that will stagnate and fail to grow.

All of this is not to say that our healthcare system is not aware of the risks and catastrophic consequences of medical errors. The Institute of Medicine's "To Err Is Human: Building a Safer Health System" brought to the forefront the need for reform in our healthcare system when it came to medical errors.[26] While my section may give off the vibe that no one has thought about medical errors in healthcare until this fantastically written book, it is far from the case. However, their argument on the importance of reporting medical errors converges nicely on the improv ideas I am espousing in this book. We must take a view of there being no real mistakes in order to feel comfortable reporting on

25. "Overcoming Obstacles to Medication Error Reporting," *Pharmacy Times*, 7 July 2016, https://www.pharmacytimes.com/view/overcoming-obstacles-to-medication-error-reporting.

26. Molla Sloane Donaldson, "An Overview of *To Err is Human:* Reemphasizing the Message of Patient Safety," In: Hughes RG, editor, *Patient Safety and Quality: An Evidence-Based Handbook for Nurses,* (Rockville: Agency for Healthcare Research and Quality, Apr. 2008), Chapter 3, https://www.ncbi.nlm.nih.gov/books/NBK2673/.

errors and thus be able to address and fix the process so that they are not repeated.

All of the improv tenets work together synergistically. When it comes to the idea of "there are no real mistakes" we can see the importance of having a shared vision and working as a team. If we remember that we are "playing" for our patients, and that winning means building the strongest, most robust system that generates the desired outcome of healthier patients, than it is easy to see why mistakes, though avoided as much as possible, must be embraced as opportunities to learn. By learning and more importantly, applying these lessons, we can have a system where our patients truly are the winners.

Chapter 10

CURIOSITY

It May Have Killed the Cat,
But It Could Save Your Patient

I got into healthcare because I was interested in and fairly good at chemistry. I was curious about chemical reactions, building molecules, and making things boil on Bunsen burners. As I progressed from high school chemistry into my undergrad course work, my curiosity waned. My desire to explore the unknown lessened. This sense of intrigue and wonderment about the world was replaced with the urgent need to pass tests. My new brand of curiosity consisted of me wondering about what would be on the test.

I did have a naïve hope that once I got to pharmacy school, there would be a renewal of interest in exploring the unknowns of pathophysiology, pharmacology, and how suppositories are made. Okay, learning about suppositories was pretty cool, and good for more than a couple laughs. However, a similar syndrome afflicted me: "Good-grades-itus." Part of this approach was out of my goals of graduating and getting accepted into a highly competitive pharmacy residency. Part of the approach was the "fire hydrant" volume of information I was expected to learn and regurgitate on a regular basis. Would I have loved to spend some time going deep into how atherosclerotic plaques are formed? Sure would have. But not when I also had to learn about pharmacy law, the kinetics of antibiotics, and dosing adjustments for kidney disease.

I am not saying that we should not be expected to learn a large amount of information in our professional schools, but we do end up covering a large breadth and not much depth. Our medical training inundates us with so much information and responsibilities that we never can follow those questions or curiosities. It's debatable whether this amount of information and responsibilities is necessary.

There is a side effect of this deluge of information and pressure for perfection in our training. We take some of the brightest and most curious minds and turn them into unquestioning robots. I know I have harped on the "don't ask questions" thing, but this gets taken to an extreme, in the wrong direction, as students are trying to learn and understand. Think back to your training and education. How often did students in class ask questions that were of an inquisitive nature and not just, "will this be on the test?"

Based on my personal experience, I'll guess that there were one or two "question askers" and about a hundred other "eye rollers at question askers." I am a little ashamed to admit, but I was probably in the "eye roller" camp. As a trainee, we revere those professors, mentors, and preceptors who seem to have all the answers and all the real-world experience. We trust their expertise, opinion, and knowledge unquestioningly. Unfortunately, this trust can be to our detriment. When a professor discusses a fact or study, and someone dares question it, there is often the eye rolling from fellow students and a condescending response from the teacher. Eventually, because of peer pressure and intimidation from authority figures, the few questioners stop asking.

I can recall being on my internal medicine pharmacy rotation, just months from graduating with my shiny PharmD, and being in a discussion room post rounds with the medicine team. We were discussing pain management options and what alternatives were left for a particular patient. Myriad medications, surgeries, and procedures had been tried, but this patient was left still in pain. Me, being a moderately curious and ever-enthusiastic pharmacy student, remembered back two months prior to my time on a rotation with the Indian Health Service. There, I had spent two days with a general surgeon who also practiced acupuncture. It was very hands-on for a pharmacy student, but not so hands-on that I actually inserted any actual acupuncture needles . . . or performed any surgeries. The surgeon discussed his training in both Eastern and Western medicine, and I saw him inserting the acupuncture needles and seeing the relief from his patients' various ailments. We went over the literature that shows evidence of efficacy for acupuncture. He also emphasized there was a time for Western medicine too: "If my appendix bursts, I am going to a surgeon." The day ended with him doing some very Western medicine, debriding wounds with topical numbing agents.

Alas, my brain was still relatively fresh with the possibilities of acupuncture. It was not a therapy I would think of first line, but it was there as something you *could* try. So, as our team discussed options for our suffering patient, and they asked if anyone had anything else, I said, "What about acupuncture?"

The attending physician wasn't sure if I was joking, and so he wasn't sure if he was supposed to laugh. Once he realized I was serious, he dismissed my suggestion fully: "There's not even anecdotal evidence that stuff works. Total waste of time."

Can you guess how many times after that I offered up a suggestion or a question?

I was embarrassed for having asked the question, and you can bet I shut down any inquiries or questions I had for the rest of that rotation. Nobody likes to feel like the dumb kid in the classroom. My story is repeated thousands of times a day, and it is not just students that learn to be quiet. One discipline shuts down another discipline. A senior provider shuts down a junior provider. There is no humility in healthcare. There seems to be no acknowledgment that the standards of care we currently practice could be doing more harm than good.

In retrospect, what would a reasonable expectation from me have been from that provider? I certainly would not have expected him to send that patient for a STAT acupuncture session. However, a simple "yes, and" of acknowledging that a pharmacy student was looking for solutions to a patient's problem as part of a team, even if that solution was less traditional, would have gone a long way in fostering my confidence as a trainee. Perhaps, I would have liked a little curiosity from him: encouragement to "show me the data" that my solution had some merit, rather than outright dismissing me. I understand that pinning my argument of fostering an environment of curiosity on a treatment that is far from "standard of care" is somewhat precarious. However, I think our patients would be better served from both a provider, and an administrative level in healthcare, if instead of the shutting down of a new or different idea, the response could be more of, "Oh, I hadn't thought of it like that. Tell me more of why your idea could work."

To question is crucial to making progress and finding newer and better ways of taking care of our patients. This is how the scientific process is supposed to work. A hypothesis is generated and then tested to be proven true or not. If we were working in a healthcare system where provider satisfaction was high, patient satisfaction was high, and outcomes were pristine, you could *almost* argue that you could justify not asking questions and recommend just being happy things are so good. Yet they are far from good.

There's an old Chinese proverb that highlights the importance of curiosity and having an environment that supports asking questions:

"The person who asks is a fool for five minutes, but the person who doesn't ask is a fool forever."

Like the brave souls in pharmacy school and like me on rotation, the person who dares ask a question is often scoffed at and called a fool. How many "conventional wisdoms" in healthcare have been wrong in the past, are currently wrong now, or will be wrong in the future and will have continued onward because we have all been conditioned to avoid playing the fool? The sad reality is that in the end, healthcare will be infinitely foolish because ineffective status quos will continue. We are afraid to question our authority figures. This will not only harm the patients we care so much about, but it will harm ourselves. The moral injury and burnout from continuing treatments, policies, and guidelines that leave us frustrated and our patients sick suck the joy from being healers.

I think a lot of us in healthcare are aware of this truth. Yet, we don't question and don't speak up about things that puzzle us or we think could be done differently. Perhaps there is more than just the concern of looking "stupid."

As I reflect on my experience asking questions as a pharmacy student, and quickly being shot down, I realize there was a significant element of shame involved. It was almost like I had lacked professionalism and should have known better than to question an attending physician. I was ashamed of *having not known*, and I think on the many times I have had to ask a colleague for their opinion or a thought on a patient issue or problem. I often find myself apologizing for asking a question (and not even in the context of an improv scene!) because I should have "just known." Perhaps this is my own experience, but I have encountered several colleagues who preface their inquiries with, "This is probably a dumb question, but . . ." We have a collective fear of shame and looking dumb. It's our culture of labeling these curious providers as "quacks" or "unprofessional" for the sin of posing a question.

The fear of these kinds of labels keeps us silent and prevents progress on our most pressing problems.

The consequences of this lack of curiosity can be two-fold. First, our healthcare providers are conditioned not to question the authority/guidelines/way things have been done. Secondly, whatever dogma is in place becomes almost impossible to budge. If it wasn't so sad, it would be funny: most of us agree our healthcare system is broken, our providers are burnt out, and our patients are not getting healthier. Yet, we are all too frozen in our status quo to speak up to make changes. Or, for those that do speak up, they are often silenced by four words that stop curiosity in its tracks and enable an attitude of elitism that crushes any sort of interdisciplinary cooperation. Those four words are: Stay in your lane.

Hell No, Don't Just Stay in Your Lane

I think it is important to have pride in your profession. I think that you should strive to be an expert in whatever it is that you do, whether it's being a physician, nurse, pharmacist, social worker, or any other of the many roles we use in our team-based approach in healthcare. Finally, I think you should not practice beyond your expertise. I, for one, promise never to give a prostate exam. You're welcome.

However . . .

Too often I see "turf wars" erupt between specialties of physicians, between nurses and pharmacists, and between any other groups with input on how to handle a problem or situation. If a nurse suggests a treatment to a physician, they are told to pipe down because they don't have the experience of treating patients. Yet, that nurse may have experience and insight that a provider might not have based on their patient rapport or experience. A pharmacist could counsel on dietary approaches to help manage their blood sugar, but are told by dieticians they shouldn't be giving advice on food. The amount of inter- and intra-professional turf war scenarios are endless, and I won't list them like Bubba from Forrest Gump listing shrimp preparations.

I promise I am getting to how improv can help alleviate our curiosity deficiency in a comprehensive manner, but the "stay in your lane" attitude brings up the importance of teamwork and group mind inherent in improv. When we squabble amongst ourselves, we stifle creativity, and in doing so, also ignore the big picture goal: taking care of the patient. Petty differences and unneeded pride in your profession getting the glory or being right ignores the urgent need to care for the patients that we fight over. More importantly, ignoring other healthcare team members' perspectives and ideas by shutting them up in "their lane" will cause us to miss or ignore crucial details in solving problems.

As an example, I was working in our GI clinic one day, when I received a request for a medication to treat a patient's Small Intestinal Bacterial Overgrowth, or SIBO for those of you who love abbreviations. I was not familiar with the providers, a lot of the medications, or the conditions treated, but such was the life of a "floater/prn" pharmacist. I received this Prior Authorization request and began to investigate its appropriateness. The indication checked out. There were no contraindications to its use, so at the very least it was safe. They had failed other, formulary medications and were still feelin' dat bloat, so it was fair to try another gun in the arsenal. Given that I had not worked on many Prior Authorizations for this drug, I turned to my warm fuzzy blanket that is UpToDate.[27] I was curious. I didn't want to just blindly approve something if there was a problem. My curiosity was rewarded by finding out that the length of treatment was incorrect. Typical pharmacist, finding out someone else's error and seeing it as a "reward." I think I need a new hobby.

Anyway, as most pharmacists reading this probably know, this was only the beginning of the story. Any ol' pharmacist can find an error. Where the rubber actually meets the road is properly and accurately communicating it to the not-always-glad-to-see-you provider, who has just been shown to have had an "error." I was nervous to bring this up to the GI provider in question. I had never actually met them, thus I had no rapport nor idea what their relationship with pharmacy was. They could be the "oh man, thanks, you guys always have my back" type, or the "I AM THE GOD OF ALL THINGS MEDICINE AND THOU SHALT NOT QUESTION MY DOSING" type. Such is the "fun" of pharmacy.

---

27. For those who are unfamiliar, UpToDate is an online drug and disease information resource.

Well, that day, I, and the patient, hit the jackpot. The provider who had entered the order was a curious soul, although I cannot confirm whether they had ever taken an improv class or read an excellent book on the subject. I opened with the good: med looks appropriate, no issues or contraindications, and the strength is A-OK. However, they needed to be treated for a different duration than they had requested for SIBO. The provider was gracious, and actually said with a smile, "I always get that length messed up, thanks for letting me know, I *probably* won't forget it in the future."

This was a provider who allowed themselves to be humble, curious, and to serve the ultimate goal: taking care of the patient. Theirs and my curiosity, as well as our ability to work well as a team, helped provide the appropriate care for our patient, all in a warm, enjoyable environment where we were both able to learn and grow. It is this synergistic attitude of working toward a common goal and getting contributions from all members of a team that helps improvisers thrive. In improv, we are out of luck if we cannot work together and rely on each other's ideas.

In healthcare, we too often alienate our team members and lose focus on our purpose. This, in turn, keeps curious minds from having any confidence or desire to suggest solutions. New innovation is slowed or stopped, and once again, the ultimate user of our services—patients—suffer.

All members of our healthcare teams, from the leaders in administration to the person seeing patients day to day can apply the lessons of group mind and teamwork to foster an environment of curiosity and idea creation that both improve their own satisfaction at work and more importantly patient outcomes. A focus within your team—from small teams up to the organizational level—need to clearly define what your "group mind" should be focusing on. From there, it should be emphasized that each member of the team is there to provide ideas and solutions to the obstacles facing your respective team. The most important part of this process is that these ideas need to be encouraged and valued. Of course, not every idea is going to be a home run; take this from someone with very few literal *or* metaphorical home runs in his career. However, if your team-based approach can string together enough smaller ideas and, to complete the analogy, a lot of singles, and they are embraced, the "aggregation of marginal gains" can take hold. This is what a great improv team does—they take every small gift that is given to each other within in a scene, embrace it with strong teamwork and a curious mind, and craft it to fit their ultimate goal: their group mind.

But it need not only be those brave souls on an improv stage. The idea of fostering a culture of curiosity by embracing group mind and teamwork seems almost too simple to write about. Yet, healthcare sorely lacks teamwork and group mind, and collective effect on reducing curiosity and innovation are hard to ignore.

Simply define your goal and support your team on the path to achieving it, leaving all ideas and solutions on the table.

Another reason for listening outside of our zones of expertise is that we often can get blinders on. As a pharmacist, when evaluating a patient or problem, I come from the perspective of "TDF" or "Think Drugs First." Given this is my area of training, it makes sense that this is my primary focus. Oftentimes, when trying to solve a patient problem with an interdisciplinary team, I will take the problem and try and fit in how a medication may be causing it. Given our epidemic of polypharmacy, this is often the case. Yet, there are times when trying the TDF approach will not yield an answer, no matter how hard I try to make it fit into the problem at hand.

This phenomenon is not limited to pharmacy. Any profession can get their blinders on, become hyperfocused on a small singular issue, and miss the forest for the trees. An opportunity then arises that someone, who may be from a different discipline and has a different perspective, could shed a new light on a problem. Our current paradigm is to ignore this alternative discipline since they aren't the "experts." A winning paradigm—and remember what "winning" in healthcare looks like—would be to agree to listen and try to see if the proposed solution is viable, safe, and a possible way to fix the problem at hand. Learning to lean on each other instead of fighting a turf war has required more humility from me, but it has led to a much greater level of job satisfaction and more solutions found. This perspective shift occurred because of the lessons of teamwork and group mind from my improv training.

These days, when I hear someone tell me to "stay in my lane" now that I have adopted an improv mindset, it may surprise you that I absolutely agree about staying in my lane. Of course, I am a smartass who has redefined what my "lane" actually is. I believe all of our lanes should be doing what we need to help improve our patients' health. See what I did there? I took my "lane" from a rural dirt road to the

Autobahn. I cannot control what other disciplines around me believe, nor their opinions on who should pipe up or pipe down when it comes to patient care.

As a *patient* in our healthcare system, I don't really care who comes up with the solutions for the problems I face. It could be a delicate procedure from a neurosurgeon or a suggestion for better sanitation from the custodial staff that improves bed turnover time and cleanliness. Recall, we are a healthcare team, we need to be able to put our egos aside and work toward that common goal of improving our patients' health and lives.

A key aspect to this interprofessional harmony is the fostering of curiosity that the improv mindset encourages. If I, a pharmacist, am more curious as to the "why" of how a physician is treating a patient, my curiosity can help pay off in the end with new knowledge I may be able to apply to my practice, as well as learning more about that physician's approach to a problem. If my curiosity is met with a "no" from another discipline, then my interest will be stifled, and I will be less apt to try and learn and apply new knowledge in the future. So, I encourage anyone reading this book who works in healthcare, to keep in mind what they can think when someone tells them to "stay in their lane."

Chapter 11

ACCEPTING REALITY TO BUILD RESILIENCE

You Can't Choose Your Circumstances, But You Can Choose Your Response

Resiliency: So Hot Right Now

Resiliency is a word that, at least in the world of pharmacists and pharmacy education, is being thrown around quite a bit. There is a crisis of burnout unique to healthcare where as many as half of clinicians are feeling burnt out,[28] and leaders are scrambling for ways to turn our trainees and employees into more "resilient" individuals in the face of our challenges. This is not without good reason, as the costs of burnout are catastrophic to the healthcare system, and include higher

---

28. William Wan, "Helath-Care System Causing Rampant Burnout among Doctors, Nurses," *Washington Post*, October 23, 2019, https://www.washingtonpost.com/health /2019/10/23/broken-health-care-system-is-causing-rampant-burnout-among-doctors -nurses/

patient risk, malpractice claims, high worker turnover, and billions of dollars lost. Not to mention the misery inflicted upon the front-line healthcare workers.

I think we could look at this burnout/resiliency crisis from a couple of angles and find that applying improv can help alleviate some of the challenges we face. First, I think a lot of the burnout comes from the top down in cultures that don't provide a work environment that supports patient care or a rewarding experience for practitioners. Some of the issues could be managers that don't listen, inflexible processes that hinder rather than help patient care, and a culture unwilling to listen to those who bring forth new ideas. Hmm, embracing a culture focused on a single goal, emphasizing teamwork, and being willing to say "yes" to new ideas. Where have we heard that before?

Oh, that's right, the "yes, and" philosophy of improv! Many of the cultural challenges in healthcare that lead to burnout are the antithesis of the culture that improv builds. It is this challenging and maladaptive culture that *leads to burnout* which then *leads to leaders* feeling the need to make their employees more "resilient."

As someone who is about to discuss a bunch of resilience-related benefits of improv and believes that resiliency is indeed important, I believe that it really wouldn't hurt to create the type of culture that incorporates many of the improv fundamentals discussed in this book. Should healthcare providers be resilient? Hell yes. Should their work environments leave them so burnt out that they are struggling for any way they can to find that resilience just to survive? Hell no.

I will provide the benefits of applied improv for personal resilience, but I won't neglect to emphasize that our leaders need to apply a heavy dose of the "yes, and" mindset for their organizations. Our work environments need to have leaders who will agree to listen to suggestions, concerns, and complaints. Leaders who provide a focused mission that goes "deeper, not wider." Leaders who don't just say, "I got your back," but who mean it and live it.

The rest of this chapter will focus on improv benefits for individual resiliency, but I hope I have made the case for applying improv at an organizational level to create a work environment that supports their employees instead of driving them to squeeze every bit of resilience out of themselves that they can.

Build Resiliency for Yourself

Before I talk about how improv can help make you a resilient human being, let's settle on a definition first. The Oxford Dictionary has a couple of definitions for "resiliency":

1. the capacity to recover quickly from difficulties; toughness
2. the ability of a substance or object to spring back into shape; elasticity.

As much as I think we all could work on our general elasticity, I think the first definition hits what we are searching for: recovering quickly from difficulties.

As I discussed briefly in this chapter, it would be swell if our employers and governing powers were a little more supportive instead of giving us the feeling that they are the ones giving us extra difficulties to deal with. Handling complex patient problems is hard enough. Handling them while also juggling a buggy and slow Electronic Health Record, incoming phone calls, Skype messages and pages (yes, I think healthcare is the last bastion of the pager), and "yearly required HR modules" is extra difficult. I advocate for fewer "difficulties" on an organizational level, and for those problems a different book is probably needed. Yet I want to be sure that as I dive into improvisation's utility in building resiliency, I'm not seeming tone deaf to the myriad challenges my fellow healthcare workers face on a daily basis. I hear you, and my wish is that these resiliency skills will be applied to taking care of patients and not your bullshit busywork.

The Harvard Business Review[29] discussed research where they identified their common traits of resilient people. Among these traits was acceptance of reality.

The name of the game in improvisation is to say "yes" to whatever is suggested or said. Our premise is an acceptance of whatever "reality" is created on stage—whether it's a suggestion you aren't familiar with or a person who does

---

29. Diane Coutu, "How Resilience Works—Improvising Your Way Out of Trouble," *Harvard Business School: Working Knowledge, Business Research for Business Leaders*, 26 August 2002, http://hbswk.hbs.edu/archive/3067.html.

not speak your language yelling and dancing on the stage. Improvisation trains our brain to accept rather than fight whatever reality is. As I have been an improviser and practicing pharmacist over the years, I have noticed (okay, I'll give credit to my wife for the observation) that I get less upset by odd challenges, stupid polices at work, and the normal dumb realities we often have to face in healthcare. A lot of credit for that needs to be given to my training in improv as I have learned, over time, the ability to simply accept instead of resisting what is presented to me.

Accept Your Reality to Be a Happier, More Resilient Human

What is it about improvisers that make us so darned happy? It could be playing with our friends on stage. It could be that we are willing to take more risks and thus reap some rewards. It could just be that improv attracts only the happiest people in society, so there is a confirmation bias, although in my experience, this is far from the truth.

To really understand how improv can make you a happier human and healthcare worker, lets first try and figure out what makes people unhappy.

A lot of unhappiness lies in wishing for a different reality. I could go into more things that people might wish for versus what their reality is, but I'll let the musical artist Skee-Lo and selected lyrics from his earworm "I Wish" explain:

I wish I was a little bit taller
I wish I was a baller
I wish I had a girl who looked good,
I would call her

. . .

I wish I had a brand-new car
So far, I got this hatchback
And everywhere I go, yo I gets laughed at[30]

It's safe to say he speaks for a lot of us who want something other than what they have right now in life. He wants to be a little bit taller. Some people want to be thinner, or have more hair, as I look at myself in the mirror. He wants to be a baller; some people wish they could just jump higher or throw a baseball harder, looking back at my seventeen-year-old self in the mirror. He wants to have a good-looking lady friend. Hey, I actually am married to a woman way out of my league, so, sorry Skee-Lo! He wants a car because he gets made fun of for his lame hatchback, which at least probably gets awesome gas mileage and is cheap to repair!

There are any number of other things we wish were different in our lives. Unhappiness is simply the chasm between what we have and what we want.

Aha! It seems this is the breakthrough on happiness/unhappiness I was seeking to explain before diving into why improvisers are happier and how improv can make you happier and more resilient too!

---

30. Skee-Lo, "I Wish," track 2 on *I Wish*, Scotti Brothers Records, recorded at Sunshine Studios, 27 March 1995.

Happiness is the difference between our reality, and the "reality" we want.

Improv can help make you happier and more resilient by working on the part of you that learns to accept and live with whatever reality you are given. The mindset of accepting reality as it comes is crucial to being a successful improviser. As an example, when we ask for a suggestion to start a scene, and all we get are things we don't know much about or don't really like, we have to make the best of it anyway. This aspect of improvisation is one of the most challenging for new students and sometimes seasoned improvisers. And based on my interactions with non-improvisers, it's a big contributor to unhappiness. There are dozens of times I can remember in which an improv student was about to start an improv scene and got a suggestion they weren't into. The look on their face was either one of panic or sheer confusion. They then looked to the other student on stage to see if they were also clueless or nervous, as they usually are. This is followed by a throat clearing and a hand going up, "Hey, uh, Cory, I don't really know much about this 'suggestion.' Can we get maybe get something else we can 'do something more' with?"

While I am sympathetic to their plight and concern, my response is usually a tad (okay, a lot) snarky and goes a little something like this, "We could do that, but is that what you are going to do when you are performing? Ask the audience for a 'better' suggestion?" I then go on to explain the importance of both honoring whatever the audience suggests to inspire their scene, but also the importance of accepting the reality provided to them.

An improviser not only has to learn to accept the reality provided to them by an audience, but also whatever happens within a scene. Oftentimes, I will hear a suggestion and have an idea of how I want to start a scene, or even if my brain is in "think ahead" mode, an idea of how I want the scene to go. In my head, it is the best idea I could think of and I just *know* it's going to be hilarious. Then, I'll step out ready to start my hilarious scene, and my scene partner will begin with something completely different. What should my next move be? The controlling side of me would want to just ignore that other person's scene initiation and roll over them with my new idea. However, the side of me trained and seasoned with the improv mindset knows what I need to do: accept the reality and "yes, and" their scene initiation. Beyond accepting the reality of our suggestions, we have to learn to accept and love the reality of whatever happens within a scene. The failure to do this can result in some ugly, unfunny scenes where it's clear that each improviser is unwilling to give up their idea. It is neither fun for the audience, nor for those within the scene. The conflict and disappointment, much like our reality outside of an improv stage, comes from the distance between the reality and what we want the reality to be.

As I write this, it is 2020, and mankind has progressed and learned to control a lot of its surroundings. There are planes and spaceships that defy gravity. We have little computers in our pockets that have more computing power than the Apollo spacecraft. And we can have nearly any product or food we want delivered to our doors—sometimes within the same day. In healthcare, we continue to innovate new procedures and medications that have made many diseases nearly nonexistent. In short, humans have enacted a lot of control on our environment. It feels pretty good, right? Suck it Mother Nature! There is a species in control, and we call ourselves humans!

However, this control, while impressive, can be fleeting and superficial. As I have mentioned, writing this book in the middle of a pandemic has shown just how little control we actually have around a lot of things. A lot of unhappiness comes from our desire to control as much as we can, and when we can't, it ruins our mood: "I just want the *perfect day* for my wedding," "If we hit all the traffic just right, we'll make it to the concert," "We only have a twenty-minute layover, but we should be *fine* to make it to Hawaii for vacation."

As a Type A pharmacist control freak, a lot of my unhappiness at work and with healthcare came from things that were beyond my control: weird questions, dumb policies, pointless meetings. As I worked through my improv training, I began to understand the importance of accepting reality and making the best of it, the old "make lemonade out of lemons" saying. Improv training helped me make that mind shift to controlling what was within my locus of control, and learning to live with whatever reality was presented with me. Instead of throwing my hands up in disgust and anger, I shrug my shoulders up and say "meh" while going to work to make the best of what is in front of me. The key is that I get to change how I think about my reality *right now*. The control is shifted not to the external events or circumstances, but how I am reacting in the moment. That is how thinking like an improviser can make us happier and more resilient in the face of our reality.

Our challenge to building individual resilience in health-care comes from the chasm of what we want and expect versus the unexpected realities we must deal with on a daily basis. Like many healthcare trainees, I expected that I would get out of my training and "change the world" one patient at a time by joining a noble profession that did the utmost to take care of those who need it. However, before I even started pharmacy school, while working as a pharmacy technician for a large pharmacy chain, I got my first taste on the side effects of wishes vs. reality.

Our store manager, who had graciously hired me, was asking me how things were going after a few weeks on the job. Admittedly, it was not the "make a difference" life affirm-ing experience I had hoped for. There was a large learning curve in the pharmacy, and the clientele were overall quite impatient. As an example, on my first day, I was struggling ringing up one of our "satisfied" customers, and as I noticed his face turning red with impatience, I offered an "info-apol-ogy," information also meant to be an apology.

Me: "I'm sorry it's taking a little longer, it's my first day. I'm still learning how everything works."

Nice Guy: "I don't care *how* long you've worked here, stop making it *my problem!*"

I wish I could recall honestly that this patient was get-ting some much-needed hemorrhoid cream, so his asshole behavior could be excused, but I can't. So I'll just say this guy was being a jerk and making a hard day even more challenging for me.

So, back to the store manager asking how things were going for me. I was mildly honest and very vague and said that I was learning a lot, and there were some challenges to deal with, but I was enjoying it—which was sort of a bending of the truth. I was afraid to dislike something I was committing my life to and to let down the person who hired me. As we were talking, I remembered noticing that she was not around the pharmacy much, considering she was a manager. Almost as if she could read the subtleties of my mind, she went on to explain something that shocked my pre-pharmacy mind but resonates now as I see myself and my peers struggle to build resilience to a profession whose expectations have let us down.

She said, in paraphrased terms from my memory fourteen years ago: "When you get into the pharmacy, make sure to kiss up to the boss as much as possible so you can get promoted. The more you get promoted, the less you have to actually be in the pharmacy working." I think she was referring to all of the "important" meetings she was attending, leaving the grunt work to her staff pharmacists.

Hearing this shocked my naïve and virgin ears. I thought the whole point of becoming a pharmacist was to like, you know, *work* in a pharmacy, not try to get out of it as much as possible. However, I quickly found out from others in the field that their goals ranged from quitting to finding something where they didn't have to work as much. Multiple pharmacists asked me, while I was a student, "Why the hell would you want to become a pharmacist?" This was a lot of cognitive dissonance to digest, but I obviously didn't alter my career path. However, years later, with pharmacist and improv experience under my belt, it's clear these same patterns are repeated in all the disciplines:

1. Go into healthcare with a noble cause.
2. Have lofty expectations of what your job will be.
3. Realize reality is much different from your expectations.
4. Become burnt out, stressed, and depressed about your career path.

How can improv help us with this? It is all about learning not only to accept the tumultuous reality, struggles, or challenges, but to *love them* and see them as gifts. Improv has taught me to rid myself of all expectations and plans on stage, and has taught me it is a fool's errand to be tied to an expectation in healthcare. Whether it is thinking a new job is going to be "pharmatopia" or thinking that the next patient is "simple and straightforward," reality has a way of reminding you that your plans are, at best, humorous suggestions for the universe to upend.

An example from my time on stage occurred when performing with my friend and founder of our local improv theater, Justin. We have a team called "Hanging Chads"—we are just a couple of bros who love improv and also a good, yet dated, presidential election reference. During a particular show, we were doing one of our normal, super hilarious sets when the person running the lights and music accidently turned their microphone on. In the middle of one of our scenes, a muffled conversation interrupted our hilarious set. To someone not trained in improv, they might have reacted with frustration in a "how dare someone mess up and distract from my show!" kind of way. Fortunately for Justin and me, we have the "yes, and" spirit and years of training to make us resilient to such an "interruption." Without missing a beat, we immediately turned that "background voice" into a part of our particular scene, justifying its existence rather than getting frustrated and wishing it would go away. We had fun with it, the audience enjoyed it, and to this day I am pretty sure that person in the tech booth has no idea of their mistake . . . I mean, gift.

Working in healthcare, we need to give up the idea we can control much of anything and be willing to give in to what happens, learning to try and "love" it as much as possible, and create gifts out of the challenges we face. One of the most frustrating aspects of working in healthcare or anywhere is when working with a colleague that, well, just wears on you. Early in my career, I had several of these that would burst into my office, even if I had a patient, because they had a question or problem that needed fixing *right now*. Granted, I have spent most of my time in primary care, where if there is a *true* emergency, it needs to be handled by the experts in the *emergency room*. Regardless, I had not yet gained this perspective, so I saw each intrusion as a violation of my professional dignity which led to frustration and soaring blood pressure.

I was trying to *control* others around me, their actions, and their personality styles. My vision for what I wanted and what my actual reality was were quite different, and it was causing me much professional angst. After years of improv training, I had the chance to work with one of these intrusive providers again. In fact, I was warned by a fellow pharmacist as to their pushy personality. This time around, though, I was armed and ready with an improv mindset that had honed my ability to let go of control and made me more *resilient* to what was to come my way. I never knew when the interruption would occur, but the well-meaning doctor would saunter over to my desk and ask if he was "interrupting anything" because he had a "real emergency" to deal with. Instead of stopping him and telling him I was busy (I was), I used my improv skill of listening intently and completely. I would let him talk until there was an awkward pause of silence, at which point he would pick back up and continue pontificating. Eventually, he would get to the problem, all while I calmly smiled, listened, and waited for the actual issue that needing addressing. I would happily address it rather than passively aggressively as in my past, and then I'd get back to the work I was actually in the middle of before interruption.

Before I continue, you might be thinking how I needed to set boundaries and not let him walk all over me. Trust me, when I was in the middle of something *really* important, I would let him know to try me again later, but I also understood the importance of developing strong relationships with those I worked with.

It really became a game to me, to be able to mindfully and calmly listen and adapt rather than get upset, which had been my default. As I have been saying, being able to give up control and react calmly and professionally is a huge aspect of resilience that has been ingrained in me because I have been able to apply my improv training. If healthcare providers were able to make this mental shift from control to listening, reacting, and adapting, their resilience could be strengthened.

In improv training, resilience is formed by focusing on the ability to embrace change, and this can be applied to those who work in healthcare. Improvisers thrive in an unpredictable, ever-changing environment. In my experience, the frustration in healthcare comes from those who try to hang on to an idea or plan they had envisioned: either what their career or job would look like down to an individual interaction with a patient.

Beyond my shift as a healthcare provider, I learned to embrace change and the unexpected in my personal life. I'll admit I am a bit of a nostalgic fool and like to hang on to my memories . . . and to recreate them at times. Whether it's a vacation I took in my younger years that I am trying to revisit as an adult, or an experience over the holidays, clinging on to tradition for tradition's sake, I have been known to try to "recreate" an experience. I don't think that this is a phenomenon unique to me. Whether it's parents taking their kids to a place that held a special meaning to them when they were kids, an insistence on an outdated holiday tradition, or buying a particular product because "that's what we've always got," the desire to control an experience is innate. The frustration almost inevitably comes when the new experience fails to live up to expectations. This process, whether on a vacation or in a patient interaction, is one way we can get burnt out. Tell me you haven't gotten burnt out over the holidays before.

A wonderful quote from the Greek philosopher Heraclitus sums up this sentiment well:

"No man ever steps in the same river twice, for it's not the same river and he's not the same man."

Heraclitus must have gotten over the need to control his vacations, holidays, and career as a philosopher well. What he is saying is that even if we go back to the same "river," the water flowing, the environment, even the weather are not the same as the first time you experienced it. Additionally, the person you were when you first stepped in that river is not the same as the one you are today. Your journey through life has shaped your opinions, thoughts, and feelings about that metaphorical "river" and you are unlikely to feel the same about it as you did the first time you stepped into it.

It reminds me of an experience my wife and I had on a vacation. She had never been to Atlanta, and I promise I wasn't trying to recreate anything there. We were staying in a hotel, and one of our hotel "treats" is to watch cable TV since we don't have it at our home, which I know is a typical Millennial move. The Adam Sandler movie *Billy Madison* came on, and we decided to indulge. Both of us growing up loved the silly style of the movie, and I can say personally that I often quoted it. Let's just say that if quoting a line about peeing your pants is cool, consider me Miles Davis. Well, we got about ten minutes into the movie, excited for the nostalgia. However, by the second commercial break, we both looked at each other and said, "Wow, this hasn't held up very well." This was sad for both of us because we had had such fond memories of it from our younger years. Alas, the environment and the people we were had changed, and as such, our opinion and reaction to watching it was different as well.

As an example of rolling with the unexpected, we were able to give up on watching it, rather than trying to "force it" and keep going, hoping we would have that spark. We are both trained improvisers, and were able to adapt to new inputs, embrace the reality, express our feelings, and change course. For the record, we ended up watching *The Sandlot*, which, in our opinion, still holds up.

See the Transformation

It is one thing to talk about my experiences on an improv stage, or as a pharmacist, or even a vacationer in a hotel room given I have had years of practice to hone my skills. It is another to see the change in *other* healthcare professionals seeing the light of improv training for the very first time. In my experience leading pharmacists, nurses, and other health-care professionals, the change is often immediate, eye opening, and for those whom I get to follow up with, persistent in improving their healthcare practice.

One of my great joys is standing in front of a room of often skeptical strangers, teaching them a few simple rules of improvisation, and seeing them find joy, have fun, and apply skills that will make them stronger healthcare providers. Since I am a pharmacist, with a license to prove it, I feel I have a license to pick on my own profession. I have worked with a lot of pharmacists, teaching them applied improv for healthcare, and the flow of our time together usually goes like this:

I start by explaining that I am a pharmacist who also does a form of comedy called improv, and they immediately become skeptical of whether I'm actually funny, and whether this time will be a total waste.

Next, I explain that everyone together in that room has the ability to think on their feet, adapt to the unknown, give up control and worry about mistakes, thrive in their practice, and yes, be at least a little bit funny.

This is met with a collective nervous chuckle, as if to say, "Well, who you are describing cannot be us, a group of Type As whose primary role is often to point out the mistakes of others while demanding perfection of ourselves. There is no time to be funny when the drive through is five deep, or I am at my third Code Blue of the night."

Staying true to my "yes, and" brand, I agree with them that on the surface, it would seem unlikely, and they are right to be skeptical. However, I promise them that for as long as we are working together, this will be a safe place to find those inner traits they have lurking without judgment. All I ask of them is to trust me.

What happens after that?

Magic.

Once these seemingly stiff healthcare professionals buy into "yes, and," along with the other rules of improv, amazing things start to happen. Sometimes the games don't go perfectly as planned. As COVID has permitted me the opportunity to adapt to a virtual world, the audio quality and remote nature can make some of my traditional games more challenging. The truly incredible response from the participants when a line doesn't get a laugh or the energy doesn't flow smoothly is to help one another out. An immediate bond is formed, and the nature of teamwork to accomplish a goal dominates.

Other times, the unexpected truly happens during a workshop, and our innate ability to utilize an obstacle to our advantage is brought to the surface. During a spirited activity on a virtual workshop, a nurse was playing a game where she had to name "Five things you say to a police officer when you are pulled over." In this game, a participant is given a random category to come up with five things as fast as they can. In her case, it was what to say when pulled over, but I have heard everything from "Five things you say to your dog in the morning" to "Five things you say to someone who cuts in front of you in line at the grocery store." Anyway, this nurse did what a lot of people do, she nailed the first three "things", no problem. Getting to "things" four and five tend to cause issues as we lose what are trying to get off the top our brains in the list. As she was summoning her fifth thing, she said randomly, "Charlotte, sit down and be quiet." The good news for her is that this game need not be literal and we counted it as her fifth "thing." The entire Zoom audience laughed, and it turns out Charlotte was her unruly dog. Yet we all thought it was a brilliant strategy to confuse a police officer into not giving a ticket.

In this case, within thirty seconds of trying improv, our intrepid nurse had learned, adapted, and applied its principles, had fun doing it, and had a smile on her face the entire time. When we debriefed the activity, she noted how difficult it can be to simply be in the moment, but by letting go and adapting to the reality around her, in her case her yappy dog, she was able to thrive. More importantly, she said she would immediately be able to apply these skills to her job as a nurse.

Hers is just one of countless examples of healthcare professionals getting their hands on improv activities in a short session and coming away with applicable skills to their day jobs. The true applicable value of even an hour of instruction is immense. However, beyond the magic found in a single session, for those in healthcare that repeatedly train their mind in the ways of improv, the benefits are long lasting and career altering.

In my experience teaching improv at our local theater in Tucson, I have had the chance to teach improv to nurses, pharmacists, doctors, lawyers, teachers, and even rocket scientists. It has been a great pleasure to get to know people from all walks of life. Improv is a truly melting pot activity that brings people of all backgrounds together where we are able to find a common joy in learning and performing. One of those incredible individuals I have met is a family physician by the name of Pete Ziegler, henceforth known as Dr. Pete.

He came into my entry-level improv class looking to get out of his comfort zone, challenge his public appearance by getting on an improv stage, and get reenergized from his professional burnout as a physician. Dr. Pete was an excellent student. Most of my Type A professionals are. He listened, incorporated feedback, and most notably was willing to humble himself with a new and challenging skill.

Dr. Pete was a joy to teach, and to my delight, he continued through our curriculum, eventually graduating to a house team where he performed as regularly as his busy physician schedule allowed. One of the great thrills as an improv teacher is taking people who are shy, believe they cannot be funny, or are looking to break out of their comfort zone and guiding them to a level of self-confidence they did not think was possible. Dr. Pete was no different. He had a childlike excitement when a new skill he was working on "hit" in a scene. He relished the moments where he forgot his day job, was totally engrossed on stage, and found flow. Perhaps my favorite part of teaching and coaching him was how he would talk excitedly about how energizing improv was for him.

But this is an improv for healthcare book, and as much as you may enjoy hearing about his improv scenes, you'd probably like to know how he thought improv impacted his day job as a physician. Well, if you are tired of my words, let me give you some of his words:

"I found new ways to connect and relate to my patients and staff using techniques . . . in improv. Learning to actively 'listen with paranoia' and pay attention to their words and energy in the moment improved my ability to meet their needs and has made me a better clinician, colleague and leader."

Well put, Dr. Pete. I don't think there is much more that I could write that could encapsulate the real-life application in healthcare that improv provides. However, one of those nurses who has learned and performed improv at our local theater, henceforth known in this book as "Nurse Amy," has a little more to say on her real-life application of improv to her experience working in healthcare:

> "Improv is the art of teamwork and agreement . . . For me, learning improv has bettered my listening skills, my ability to think on my feet, my capacity to interact effectively with others, and my capability to take what is thrown at me and make it work. In nursing, these are all essential skills because no matter how much you learn in school or during your preceptorship, you will *never* be ready for everything that a day on the hospital floor will throw at you. Being able to work with what you have for the best outcome is a skill that comes with time and experience—but an improv class or two can certainly speed up the process."

Ultimately, improv teaches us to let go of control and turn the unexpected into a gift—like an unexpectedly hot microphone or a different choice in movie while on vacation. This skill breeds resilience in other facets of our lives. For those who work in healthcare, learning and applying this improv skillset, while not fixing the problems inherent in our system, will help us be happier, more resilient, and more able to deal with the challenges we face, even turning them into opportunities for growth, collaboration, and innovation. You will learn to love your reality instead of wishing for something else. The best part is it is just a simple mindset shift that can be inspired by improv. Should you give it a try? Yes, And!

Chapter 12

GROWTH MINDSET

How Improv Destroys Limiting Beliefs and Gets You Thinking Big

Let Improv Change Your Life

Thus far, I hope I have provided evidence of the utility of improv in its application on making the healthcare experience better for its consumers and providers. From the day-to-day, face-to-face interactions with patients to the policymakers, there is room for improv's tenets to be applied. If the book stopped now, I think there could be much utility found in the lessons I have described. However, the book doesn't stop here!

Because if you have made it this far, you are hopefully seeing improv as a useful tool for healthcare, and you want to know more about how to apply it, and more there is! While improv helped make me a better pharmacist, I believe improv helps develop better human beings too. I know it has made me a better one: a better listener, communicator, empathizer, and team player, as well as more resilient. These skills don't just help me as a pharmacist. I apply them to my roles as father, husband, friend, teammate, neighbor, and every other role I find myself in. As my improv training has unfolded, the lines between the stage and life have blurred, and I have found myself applying these lessons and tenets to my everyday life. Beyond being a pharmacist, I'm a happier and more complete human being. I'm hearing things in conversations I had missed before. I'm having more fun in the mundane banalities of life.

I am *happier*.

With the benefit of hindsight, I realize what had happened. Before I took improv, I was a Type A pharmacist who lived life by trying to control as much as I could, living by the book, and following my "plan." Yet, I was lacking *something* else. Something that helped guide my decisions and beliefs. That was, until I found improvisation and realized that it's not just a form of theater. It's not just a "hack" to make healthcare better.

It is a life philosophy.

This chapter is all about how the "philosophy of improv" or the "philosophy of yes, and," if applied, can help guide you through life a happier and better human. Let's break it down!

Build a Growth Mindset

Perhaps you have heard the term "Growth Mindset" thrown around. Perhaps you even know what it means. Maybe, you even know what the opposite of it is, the "Fixed Mindset." I think improv as a life philosophy helps to foster a Growth Mindset. So, let's take a moment to define it and then jump into why improv is so effective at helping you achieve it.

In *Mindset: The New Psychology of Success*,[31] Carol Dweck lays out how the beliefs we carry about ourselves are related to how we view our own personality. I'll start with the Fixed Mindset and then contrast it to the Growth Mindset I am touting as a side effect of improvisation. A Fixed Mindset "assumes that our character, intelligence, and creative ability are static givens which we can't change in any meaningful way, and success is the affirmation of that inherent intelligence, an assessment of how those givens measure up against an equally fixed standard; striving for success and avoiding failure at all costs become a way of maintaining the sense of being smart or skilled." Alternatively, a Growth Mindset "thrives on challenge and sees failure not as evidence of unintelligence but as a heartening springboard for growth and for stretching our existing abilities."[32]

When I look at healthcare, and those who inhabit it, I see a whole pile of Fixed Mindset going on. Those with a Fixed Mindset work hard to look as smart as possible, which has me thinking of those attending physicians "pimping" all of the residents on rounds. Other ways that those with a Fixed Mindset try and "protect" their intelligence is to ignore or avoid criticism since it could prove they were wrong. They also tend to feel threatened by the success of others . . . again, it could make them look bad.

---

31. Carol S. Dweck, *Mindset: The New Psychology of Success*, (United States: Random House, 2006).

32. Maria Popova, "Fixed vs. Growth: The Two Basic Mindsets That Shape Our Lives," *brainpickings*, https://www.brainpickings.org/2014/01/29/carol-dweck-mindset/.

I highlighted this idea of being threatened in my section discussing the "stay in your lane" syndrome that plagues healthcare. There is a fear amongst the different disciplines of "looking bad" if someone else figures out a problem that was "their" specialty. However, as I have emphasized, "winning" is when the patient is put first and they improve. It should not matter if the cardiologist, radiologist, or respiratory therapist figures out a problem. It should matter if the problem is solved. Yet if healthcare and its providers are stuck in a Fixed Mindset, this will not be the case. All the different players will revert to playing "defense" for their own specialty and their egos.

Ultimately, those with a Fixed Mindset believe there is only "so much intelligence" in each person and thus they will limit themselves in what they can achieve. They'll avoid challenges for fear of looking bad, but it's in life's challenges that we grow to become more intelligent, strong, and resilient. The Fixed Mindset can also be projected onto others. The idea of a limited intelligence or ceiling of capability happens often when patients are "typecast" into being "difficult," or "unable to listen" and "non-compliant." We as providers are as guilty of having a Fixed Mindset as we are of assuming others are limited as well, like when we assume that a patient will never change their diet, quit smoking, or take their medications regularly. I hope I have made the case that having a Fixed Mindset is not optimal for the outcomes of our patients, our own personal lives, or for the growth and improvement of healthcare in general.

Unleash Your Growth Mindset

I think we delved into what the Fixed Mindset is, and why it is detrimental. Let's dive into a Growth Mindset and see how the philosophy of improv can help to unleash it for you and your patients!

Those with a Growth Mindset believe that intelligence can be developed. Right off the bat, you can see that the limiting belief of being only "so smart" or "so good" at something is nonexistent in these individuals. Improv helps to move people toward this belief in growing skills and intelligence by getting them into situations that they never thought they could navigate successfully. I have had more people who say they are "introverts," "bad speakers," and "not funny" prove within a few minutes of a class or workshop that they could be great at *all three*! One of my friends at our improv theater could barely speak on stage. She would get nervous and say "sorry" in the middle of a scene. She pushed through the discomfort and has gone on to perform, teach, and coach—all because she busted through her limiting beliefs! Improv removes self-imposed limits, and does so in a safe and supportive environment so that people feel comfortable taking risks. Improv proves to you that you can develop skills you thought you didn't have or couldn't do, and it puts you in a Growth Mindset.

Getting through any sort of medical training is challenging, that I will not argue. However, those with a Growth Mindset continue to seek out challenges rather than avoid them with the fear of "looking dumb." I can say from my own experience as well as the stories of several of my peers, that a lot of us got through pharmacy school and just wanted to get a job once it was over. I did a residency and got a couple of board certifications, but for a long time I lacked the desire to seek out additional challenges. I was of the mindset that I had done enough training and learning, and it was time to sit back and take care of my business at work. Once I started into my improv journey, however, I started challenging myself on stage, with new characters, accents, and show formats. Getting on stage in front of strangers with no script is in itself a challenge. It's also through the challenges on stage that I gained confidence in my ability to tackle other challenges in life, both personal and professional. Too often I see those in healthcare get into a pattern of punching in and punching out without the desire to take on a new challenge. Sometimes this is a lack of time. Okay, it's probably a lot of lack of time, but there is still that limiting belief holding them back from trying new things and challenging themselves.

Improv training forces you to challenge yourself, and, once adopted as a life philosophy, opens many new doors because of a willingness to be open to difficult things. It is because of this Growth Mindset trait of seeking out challenges that I have written this book, presented numerous pharmacy CEs on very nontraditional topics, and worked on building a business of my own. I had some very limiting beliefs early in my career that have been completely overcome thanks to training my brain in the "improv way" of seeking out challenges. The rewards have been a richer and more fulfilling life and career.

Improvise to Overcome Obstacles

It is inevitable that we will face setbacks and roadblocks in our career. For those with a Fixed Mindset, they are a reason to give up, easily. Those who have adopted a Growth Mindset are resilient and continue to strive in the face of setbacks. In the words of the fictional, yet inspirational character Rocky Balboa, "It ain't about how hard you can hit. It's about how hard you can *get hit* and keep moving forward." This quote sums up the mindset it takes to be successful and makes me wanna run through a wall. It also characterizes what improv helps ingrain in you when dealing with a setback. I have learned to keep working through roadblocks on a number of levels thanks to improvisation, and I think it is a useful "muscle" to build for you too.

First, when learning any new skill or craft, there are going to be setbacks. Whether it's learning to play a guitar, remodeling an old car, or trying to make people laugh on stage, there will be bumps along the way. Unique to improv is the team support you receive as your "group mind" helps pull team members forward in their pursuit of the craft. There is a learning curve in improvisation, but when those stumbling blocks come, the culture is one that helps lift you up and help you learn to get through it. From that comes a feeling of accomplishment that translates to confidence in overcoming other roadblocks and challenges in life.

Improv also taught me the humility to deal with a setback. It is very easy to have a great show in a theater filled to capacity one night, then completely bomb to a crowd of five the next night. When you can *see* how unamused each person is . . . that hurts. I understand improv is "disposable comedy." It happens once and never again. So I know not to get too high with the good times or too low with the bad times. This experience has served me when dealing with setbacks at work, and in life, because I have learned to understand that each experience, good or bad, is temporary. So whether I experience a setback on stage or in my pharmacy office, I know I have the skills to press on with the comfort of knowing that the issue is temporary and I have the ability to learn and grow from it.

Improv, as I have discussed, teaches resilience in the face of the unexpected setback or challenge. It fosters those challenges because with the repetitions on stage, or in a class or workshop, in a supportive environment, we experience personal growth as we become more able to deal with those challenges.

Incorporating Criticism

Being able to not only *hear* criticism, but to *listen, understand,* and *apply* it are traits of the Growth Mindset. It makes sense that for one to grow and become better, they would be willing to listen to the feedback of others who can objectively observe them, identify areas to improve upon, and provide them with that valuable information. In healthcare, we often "don't wanna hear it." Too many times I have seen providers let their degrees do their talking and arguing. While we have an impressive amount of training, we also all have blind spots no matter how many degrees you possess or letters after your name. The wise person willing to grow, learn, and ultimately become their most successful self is willing to apply feedback and criticism.

Improv taught me all about hearing feedback and criticism. Every new student, regardless of their place in life professionally or personally, is subject to the same rules of the stage. I have seen stages shared with rocket scientists, nurses, high school students, lawyers, teachers, and real estate agents—and they all were subject to the same rules and criticisms in trying to grow and improve their craft. The challenging thing about hearing criticism is that our egos do not like it. Maybe some of us had a bad experience with being provided criticism in too harsh or direct a manner. These are valid concerns, but as I have discussed, the supportive team atmosphere of improv lends itself to being open to learning to receive feedback. The stakes are very low, people laugh or they don't, you can be vulnerable with trying something new, and the muscle of receiving criticism is strengthened.

What's the result of openly accepting criticism? Personal and professional growth and growth in whatever endeavor you approach with a mindset to accept feedback and criticism. How much do you feel you have grown in your role as a healthcare provider? In your life in your other roles? If you are able to apply the improv mindset of seeking out feedback and then incorporating the feedback, you will find yourself a much more complete and better person than before. I don't think healthcare has grown in the right ways. Clearly the scope and money spent on it has grown immensely, but those who practice and the models that we work under have not. I think it is the Fixed Mindset idea of being closed to feedback and criticism that is holding us back. Let's start using the "yes, and" philosophy to heed our criticism, in fact, welcome it, so we can grow and be better providers for our patients.

Find Joy in the Success of Others

I'll wrap this up on how improv leads a Growth Mindset by discussing a final point: those with a Growth Mindset find lessons and inspiration from the success of others. Let's take a moment and be reeeeeal honest with ourselves. Have you ever seen someone achieve success professionally and felt jealous? Threatened? Angry it wasn't you getting recognized for your hard work? Don't feel bad, because I have been there myself thinking, "I just *know* I'm smarter/harder working/a better pharmacist than that person." I think we have all had those moments. Within healthcare we are not immune to the jealousy of others success. How did I, and how can you, flip this sentiment around?

We can ask ourselves: what would an improviser do? Remember, improv is a team sport. It taught me the importance of working together with a group mind toward a common goal. Performing improv also serves as a constant reminder of what "winning" looks like—the team succeeding. Often times a scene calls for you to provide that "alley-oop" pass to another performer who gets the punch line, the laughs, and the glory. If an improviser sat back and stewed in anger after assisting another teammate, they would not be long for that team. Like a Growth Mindset, improvisers find joy in the success of others. There have been multiple improvisers who have left our theater and gone on to bigger markets and more notoriety. Part of me (in the past) was jealous I was still in Tucson, working as a pharmacist, while they were off living the dream. Yet, I have reminded myself to step back and understand that their success helps me as a fellow improviser and member of the same theater together.

Now, when I see my improv theater alumni doing amazing work, or others teaching improv to professionals, both things I wished I was doing, I no longer get jealous, I get excited and inspired. Everyone who has success around you, whether its pharmacy, improv, or writing books, can be inspiration for you to strive for. You can learn from them, from their mistakes and triumphs along the way so that your path to success is faster.

What we need to be able to apply, then, is the ability to learn lessons from the success of others in our personal and professional lives. The philosophy and application of improvisation can teach us how the success of the team is really a way to find success ourselves. If you are working in any particular field as a physician, nurse, pharmacist, or a particular institution, and a colleague has a breakthrough, a successful project, or a great new idea accepted by leadership, it is incumbent on us to be happy for them. The axiom "a rising tide lifts all boats" should be remembered and taken to heart. This attitude of gratitude will help foster the Growth Mindset, opening you up to new ideas and possibilities.

Gratitude for others' success is not limited to our professional lives. Whether we see our friends find professional success, parenting success, or any other sort of life breakthrough, remember to let that serve as inspiration for your own journey, rather than stewing in jealousy.

My goal in taking a side trip down the "Growth Mindset" path was to show you how applying improv as a life philosophy both personally and professionally can help foster growth in you. Being open to criticism, learning to try new and challenging things, keeping after it even when facing setbacks, and using the success of others as inspiration are all skills I learned from my years as an improviser. I can say that my mind shift from a Fixed to a Growth Mindset has, indeed, opened many new doors and led to much greater personal and professional satisfaction in life. While at my core I will always have my controlling Type A pharmacist brain, improv has helped me develop my risk-taking and adventurous "right brain." Old Type A Cory would never have thought to write a book, have kids, or pursue a career teaching the application of improvisation. While I certainly have not achieved all of my goals in these areas, the lessons, connections, and *new learning* I have achieved have made for a deeper, richer, and more satisfying life. I owe these experiences to improv, and I think you can find the same growth by applying the "yes, and" philosophy to your life as well.

The Growth Mindset is but one of the many advantages of adopting an improv mindset. Let's move on to something that many of us adults fail to do: play.

Chapter 13

PLAY MORE

*Because You Already
Work Enough*

Healthcare Shouldn't Have to Feel Like Work

"That's why it's called work, not play."

This is my dad's advice when I complain about work. My guess is that any of you reading this with an "old school" family member have been given similar advice. I am willing to accept this, to a degree. Yes, when we go work for an employer, there is an expectation of the tasks we will accomplish, policies we will adhere to, and time we will spend doing both of those. I am not arguing that we should get paid to just do whatever we want, whenever we want, however we feel. But why does work, and specifically for those of us in healthcare, have to *feel* like such work?

What sort of feeling am I talking about? To some degree, I think the air of "professionalism" tamps down on the inclination to have even small amounts of silliness and fun. The adherence to "this is the way X profession should act" stifles creativity and new or different ideas. The opportunities to "play" at work are minimal. Although any sort of neurological surgery *is* a sort of riddle, I won't try to convince you that trying to solve a riddle in the middle of a brain tumor removal is a good idea, but encouraging banter and activities to make healthcare a bit more playful *is* a good idea.

Why do we need to have more fun and play in healthcare? Healthcare can be an incredibly stressful, difficult, and depressing environment to work in. We are tasked with taking care of the sick, comforting their families, and coming face to face with mortality. There should be no shame in having these and other difficult feelings since we deal with such difficult, deep human experiences. Injecting a bit of fun and play into work can help alleviate these feelings. Having something enjoyable or fun to look forward to can make coping with these challenges easier.

From a practical standpoint, play can help us *be better* at our jobs. I'll let the famous Mr. Fred Rogers (yes, *that* Mr. Rogers) explain:

> "Play is often talked about as if it were a relief from serious learning. But for children, play is serious learning."

Okay, you are saying, "Hold on. He is referencing children. We are not children; we are adults working in highly stressful healthcare jobs!" On that point, I will not try to argue. However, taking a step back, we can realize the value in "make believe" or role play. Children, in safe environments, can play, make up games, and *fail* at things. These all provide opportunities to learn and grow. So, actual learning is happening during play. Now, fast forward to adulthood, put us in the world of healthcare under the umbrella of "professionalism" and play vanishes. All of our learning becomes serious: continuing education, Journal Clubs, Grand Rounds presentations. None of these stoke a bit of excitement in me as I type them. In fact, I was able to hear your collective groan as you read those words. I am sorry for conjuring up such boredom. But that is the key: boring presentations aren't fun or enjoyable, no matter how much good information they contain.

Our opportunities for "adult play" are nearly nonexistent, and thus our chances to grow individually from playful interactions are severely limited. This is one problem that improv can address directly: improv is *literally* an opportunity to put play into action! I won't repeat the lessons of learning new skills in a safe environment that improv provides. However, by either directly practicing improv games, or at least adopting a playful "yes, and" attitude to our work environment, we can get these "play reps" in. This helps us twofold: first, it provides those unscripted learning opportunities to grow our "soft skills"—listening, communication, teamwork, etc. These are essential skills that can be improved through role play like improv.

Second, injecting some playfulness into our daily work environment would make our days, dare I say it, more enjoyable. More fun. Heck, even a bit playful. I think this should be encouraged to help break the monotonous, mundane, repetitive culture that is the norm inside of healthcare. Finding a way to "make a game" of the boring, seemingly pointless tasks that can wear down our happiness, empathy, and humanity. (Okay, with the wrong Electronic Health Record, there are a *lot* of pointless tasks.)

Let me give you an example of how the play I learned from improv transferred into a more enjoyable workplace experience.

As I have alluded to, there are some monotonous tasks that are involved in our jobs. Despite the glamorous life that shows like *ER*, *Grey's Anatomy*, and *Scrubs* (okay, *Scrubs* was just really funny, and nothing like real life) portray, most of our time is spent pumping numbers into a medical record and not pumping on someone's chest to save their life. One of my less glamorous tasks is sending, via instant message, the dates and times of my patients' future appointments to our medical assistant. I have had a number of different assistants over my career, and they all were quite capable at their jobs of scheduling patients. Most of the interactions went something like this:

Me: "Please schedule Mr. X on July 14th at 9:00 a.m. Thank you"

Medical Assistant: "Done."

Me: "Thanks!"

Medical Assistant: "Welcome."

This was a conversation that was repeated multiple times a day for multiple years. Over and over and over again. It was monotonous and robotic. The job got done, but the job got old and felt more like a chore with every seemingly scripted interaction. The monotony continued on and on and on, until I was assigned a new medical assistant.

Immediately, he showed signs of applying improv. He noticed my "avatar" on Skype was the Chicago Cubs logo— he was listening intently even with his eyes. This inspired conversations about Chicago, the Cubs, baseball in general, and travel. We were able to find mutual interests and had brief, yet informative conversations unrelated to work, but that would enhance our working relationship. His curiosity and ability to observe and listen were key in quickly developing rapport.

One day, this "improv flavored" working relationship improved even more when he applied the philosophy of "work of play." We were going about our normal day, and I had asked him via Skype to schedule a patient for me, part of the normal "mundane" tasks of the day that I had mentioned previously. Instead of simply saying "complete," he responded with "Bottom of the ninth, bases loaded, two outs, full count and that one is . . . OUTTA HERE!"

I did something I rarely do when scheduling patients: I smiled.

And not just a little grin, or a bit of an up curled lip. This was a full-on, teeth-flashing smile. I may have even let out an audible, "YEAH BABY," with a fist pump. Holy Cow! This guy was *playing*. So, as an improviser, what do you think I did next? Well, I "yes, anded" him!

I responded, "And the crowd goes wild! Wrigley Field is rocking, and they are still on their feet."

We were having fun at work. We were playing. And, for those of you keeping score at home, we were still getting our needed work done! The fun didn't stop there though. We were going deeper, not wider. Later, when I asked him to schedule another patient of mine, he responded:

"Swing and a miss. Strike one. Try again"

This was no walk-off home run. Something was wrong. I looked at the message I had sent and realized I had given a date and time but forgotten the name of the patient. So, I sent a message back:

"Mr 'X' has trouble with the slider away."

He responded: "Base hit up the middle!"

And so the rest of our day went. Subsequently, we had scheduling conversations that were football themed, basketball themed, and movie themed. All in the spirit of "yes, and" and in play. More importantly, it has made what used to be a repetitive, robotic task actually enjoyable. I look forward to our interactions. I don't mind doing the boring tasks because we are able to make it fun. It remains professional. The patients get taken care of. We get to make work *enjoyable*. All of this because one of us was not afraid to inject a little play into work, and I was able to "yes, and" the prompt.

I won't sit here and write to say you must turn every task into a game at work or in life. However, the benefits of injecting playfulness into your day, to "gamify" the boring, can provide benefits on multiple levels. On the surface, it can just make boring things less boring and even close to fun. On a deeper level, as I have discussed, the "work of play" can help us develop interpersonal skills that translate to being more effective communicators, empathizers, and listeners. These playful experiences can have serious benefits. Applying the philosophy of improvisation to insert play into your life can, at best, help you realize these personal skill improvements, and at worst, you will have more fun in your life.

As I hope you are beginning to see, improv is not only a useful skill, a way to improve our healthcare experience, or a fun way to spend a Friday night out. Improvisation, when broken down to its core, is a life philosophy that is easy to adopt and apply. It helps to make you happier, a better communicator, a person who has a Growth Mindset instead of limiting beliefs, and someone who just knows how to play. When viewing the world through "improv colored glasses," you are able to adapt to challenging situations more effectively, be a better teammate, whether that team is your place of business or your own home with your family, and just be a more fun person. While I hope you, the intrepid and curious reader, find some nuggets of improv wisdom to apply to your life from this book, I also hope some of you are trying to adopting the "yes, and" philosophy. I know that it has given me something to lean on and look to for inspiration and guidance on the good times and the not so good. Most importantly, it has made me a happier person.

IMPROV SAVES LIVES

Your Call to Action

We have covered a lot of ground on the intersecting worlds of improv comedy, healthcare, and even some personal development. My hope is that you come away from reading this book a little more prepared to adopt an improv mindset in your personal and professional life. My primary goal when writing this book was to help you, the reader, see how applying the philosophy of improv comedy creates a more rewarding healthcare experience for providers and patients. A secondary goal was to see how many times I could type the words "yes, and" next to each other in a book. Can I rest assured that my secondary goal was met? *Yes, and* I hope that primary goal was met with success as well.

What happens if we don't adopt these skills?

Well, I think we would be depriving ourselves and our patients the experience we both deserve. More importantly, however, is that if we are unable to think like an improviser, we as healthcare professionals will miss the opportunity to improve the health of our patients and ultimately save lives.

You did get into healthcare to save lives, right?

Think back to the sobering statistics of the dollar and human cost of medical errors. What if we could communicate more effectively to prevent these errors? What if we were more willing to accept and acknowledge when a process, medication, or procedure is doing more harm than good? What if we were able to truly work as a team to put the patient first?

An improv comedian *can* communicate effectively, embrace the opportunity to turn mistakes into opportunities, and knows the only way to accomplish their task of making complete strangers laugh is to play together as a team.

Improvisers know what winning looks like, and I think we in healthcare have lost sight of that. It's okay though, because you have read this book. You now realize the simple approaches you can take with your practice or organization to get back on track. To focus on the business we got into: saving lives.

Adopt the Philosophy of Improv

If you stuck with me and read all the way to the end, I wish I could say there was some nugget of extra knowledge that will set you apart and turn your job in healthcare into the most fun and rewarding one in the world. The reality is your nuggets of knowledge were along the path to finishing this book.

If you can remember a few keys about improv and apply them to your professional or personal life, I think you *will* find that you and your patients have more rewarding experiences. You will have more meaningful interactions and find more meaning in your work. You will connect with your coworkers. You will welcome new ideas and innovation with the understanding that even if they may not come from your particular discipline, they could help your patients in the end.

So, let's hit a few of the high points so you can go out with some actionable improv knowledge to make yours and your patients' lives better!

First, if I have not typed it enough, here it is again: "Yes, and." These are not just two words. They are the foundation of this philosophy. Having a "yes, and" mindset means you will agree to listen and build together. If you can do that, you will build incredible things: ideas, innovations, and relationships.

Improv helps to get inside the perspective of others. It helps develop the "muscle" of empathy. Being able to say "yes, and" to patients' concerns, listening deeply, and understanding where our patients' and colleagues' challenges and desires lie will help bring satisfaction to both the providers and users of healthcare. By learning and applying the skill of empathy, you will be able to find the "why" and the "want" of your patients, and if you happen to be a manager, your employees. Providing good healthcare is not simply just demanding patients follow our advice. It is seeking out what they are feeling, what motivates them, and how we can then tailor our expertise to their situation. Improv teaches these empathetic skills.

Next, listen. Listen again. And listen some more. The key to finding joy and success in healthcare is to listen to those around us: our colleagues, our patients, our patients' family and friends. We sometimes mistakenly think the answers lie deep within our own heads. In reality, the answer is out there, floating out of the mouths of our patients or written in their body language. By applying the improv skills of listening intently, you will find the answers that you and your patients seek.

Improvisation is a team sport. It takes a group of people focusing on a common goal and developing "Group Mind" to work together to achieve their vision. This means that success involves clearly defining what "winning" looks like, putting their egos aside, and finding ways to complement each other. There is no room for the metaphorical "ball hog" because it takes humility and support to be successful. These tenets are as true for an improv team as they are for a healthcare team. Unfortunately, I think we have lost our way in healthcare and forgotten what "winning" is truly about: making our patients lives better by improving their health. There is a definite challenge in healthcare to put our egos aside and work toward our common goal. Each discipline and specialty has its own vested interests. This fact I will not refute. However, if each special interest realized it was in their best interest to apply the improv mindset and work together, our patients would truly win.

Improv promotes curiosity by encouraging an environment of idea sharing and innovation. Our healthcare environment fails to support and nurture curiosity due to its "culture of no." Learn to apply the improv mindset of exploration and curiosity to your personal practice and your personal life. We often cling to the status quo in healthcare, but it's the curiosity of the few that create the innovations that change how we care for our patients. Foster that curiosity in yourself to find new ways of improving a process at work, or exploring a drug interaction or side effect you hadn't seen before. Recall it's the curiosity of science and healing that drove so many of us into healthcare. Use the improv mindset as your inspiration to follow your own curiosity and support it in others.

Remember to create a "Culture of Yes." It becomes very easy to slip into "no-itis" where our default answer to any request, suggestion, or idea is a resounding "no." This attitude trickles into our life away from work and becomes our default answer to new plans with friends or family. Having a Culture of Yes means that you, your colleagues, those above and below you on the food chain at work know that their ideas will at least be heard. Does the ultimate answer always have to be yes? That would be an unfair expectation. Yet, more innovation, more bold ideas, and more satisfaction will come from a culture and attitude that will listen to new ideas and possibilities.

Finally, remember that improv is not just a form of theater or a "hack" to be better at your particular job, although it is technically both of those things. It is a way of approaching the world. It is a way of handling problems. It is a *philosophy*. The philosophy of improvisation promotes a Growth Mindset that helps you break away from your limiting beliefs about yourself. It supports the notion of playfulness. It helps you be a happier human being.

Really, that is what we need to do in healthcare. Treat our patients and ourselves like human beings. We have dehumanized healthcare to the point where our patients are nothing but diagnoses, prescription numbers, or X-ray images. We have lost the art of connecting with our patients on a human level, because we have focused on the robotic memorization and regurgitation our medical system demands of us.

Improv teaches us to connect on a human level, and it can help us *humanize* healthcare. It helps us stop taking care of *patients* and start connecting with *people*.

Improv truly gives us *permission to care*.

In my journey, I have gone from the depths of self-doubt, despair, and frustration with our impersonal, unfeeling healthcare system to learning to connect with those I care for and work with, finding joy in the work that I do, and ultimately creating a more rewarding experience for my patients and myself.

We got into healthcare because we thought it would be rewarding to heal our patients. We got into it to literally *save lives*. Our training and our environment have not given us the tools to find this joy in our work. Until now. Your path to a more rewarding healthcare experience can be yours if you are ready to apply the philosophy of improv.

All you need to do is say yes . . . and.

Acknowledgments

If you have made it to this section, my guess is you have come to realize that improv and healthcare are team sports. You know what else is a team sport? Writing a book! So, at this point I would like to thank the "team" of people it took to bring this book to print:

First, I have to thank the incredible team at Mandala Tree Press. To take on such a unique project requires a leap of faith and the ultimate "yes, and" commitment. A debt of gratitude goes to Azul Terronez for the time he spent answering all of my, and most importantly, my wife's questions. Being a first-time author, it was truly a pleasure putting this book in your hands to help get from start to finish. Thank you for believing in me.

To the editors who helped mold, shape, and ultimately get the finished product you read today, thank you. Thanks to Ann Maynard for your direction, fast turnaround, and many *Simpsons* references. I really think this book has everything coming up Milhouse. To Kim Karpowitz, thank you for providing the road map and direction to make sure everything that needed to be done on time was, in fact, done on time. I would also like to thank the other editors: Catherine Christensen, Justin Greer, Valene Wood, and Kaitlin Barwick.

The road to writing a book starts with a first step, and for me that first step on my improv journey started with the other half of my improv duo "Hanging Chads," the founder of the Tucson Improv Movement, and my dear friend, Justin Lukasewicz. Thank you for teaching me the magic that improv can bring on and off the stage, and for letting me be part of the incredible community you have built in Tucson. I don't know where I'd be if I didn't step into the back room of that Yoga studio/massage parlor in 2013, but I *can* tell you I'd have missed out on the approximately 100 million bits we've had since then. I got your back.

To the rest of my friends and fellow improvisers with whom I have shared the stage, sweaty summer Tucson rehearsals, and late nights at the Spool parties, thank you for making my life richer, full of laughs, and always having my back.

Taking a step out of the traditional path of a pharmacist and building another life based on improv is not easy, and I would not be here writing these words and fulfilling my dreams if not for my friend Alex Barker. Thank you for your wisdom, encouragement, and sarcasm. You always seem to know what to say to keep me going when I just want to take the blue pill and stop pushing.

A special thanks to Brian Bisher, who has taken what was a chance appearance on a podcast and turned it into a full-fledged friendship and support system. Your ability to listen and help me focus on the right mindset has got me back on the path more times than you know. I can't wait to watch the Cubs destroy the Reds with you soon.

I have already thanked my editors, but I have to thank Scott Keith, my first pharmacy boss, briefly my roommate, and the first person to read my book. Thank you for your witty edits, the hours watching YouTube and eating popcorn on those slow Target nights, and for making the move to Tucson. Sharing time with you, Kendra, and Miles is one of life's biggest highlights. "Very much now."

Writing a book can be stressful and fill you with doubt. Thanks to my friend Zaq Race for the exercise breaks and hours of stimulating political, social, and life discussions. You are a wonderfully unique human, and I am so glad you have made your way into my life. Someday, I may just let you beat me on the racquetball court. But probably not.

Pharmacy can be a frustrating profession. A big thanks to my friend and counterpart on the basketball court, Kendrick Murphy for all of the texts, memes, and *Seinfeld* quotes that lighten up even the toughest days. You are one of the finest people I have ever met. Ashville got a real steal with you.

Writing and pharmacy are not usually associated with each other. We pharmacists usually just want science, science, and more science. Fortunately, we have to do *some* liberal arts before pharmacy school, and because of that I got to learn from one of the best, Dr. Ronald Miller. It takes guts to have a "Swear Word Day," at a school in the Bible Belt, but you pulled it off, you sonofabitch. Thanks for teaching me the joy of writing, how to show no fear in being your authentic self, and all the meals at Yesterday's. YEAH!

Teaching improv, especially to healthcare professionals, is a fun challenge that I relish. The moments when a student gets "it" and applies "it" and the light bulb goes on are worth the late nights, travel, and time away from my family. Few have got "it" more than Dr. Pete Ziegler. Thank you for your passion, enthusiasm, and embodying what living the "yes, and" life really means. Healthcare would be better with more doctors like you.

I would like to send a special thanks to Drew Tarvin, who has spent more of his free time than he probably should have answering my questions on how to forge a path speaking and getting my message out to the world.

To all my friends, family, and complete strangers who have come to fill the seats at one of my improv shows, especially during the summer in Tucson, especially when the theater didn't have air conditioning, thanks for coming out for a laugh and a sweat. Just thought you should know, the theater does have A/C now. And booze!

A big thanks to anyone who has said "yes, and" to having me come talk to your group. It takes a leap of faith to have an "improv pharmacist" come speak at your healthcare organization, but I appreciate you taking a chance and joining in the fun.

Who does that leave to acknowledge? Oh yes, the big ones: my incredible family.

Setting and striving for goals has always been ingrained in me, and to that I owe a huge thanks to my parents. Thank you for always loving me, supporting me, and providing a caring ear to vent to. Thanks for the long drives to baseball games, always doing your best to raise me right, and for the hard decision in encouraging me to go across the country for college to set me on the path I find myself today. I only hope I can live up to the standard you set as parents with my own kids.

Which brings me to my own kids. Jacob and Henry, thank you for being able to turn a frustrated late night into a morning full of smiles. You two are sweeter and more fun than I could have ever imagined way back when I could never have imagined having kids. Your spirit of love and play reminds me we are all born with the ability to live in the moment and find joy and wonder in everything. Thank you for being such tough, lovable little warriors.

To Cassie, what more can I say? I get to live out my dream every day that I wake up next to you. Thank you for being such an incredible mother to our boys, and giving me the space to pursue this little dream of mine. I could not have dreamed a life as sweet as this with you . . . and we're only beginning.

About the Author

CORY JENKS earned his doctor of pharmacy degree from the University of South Carolina in 2011. Since then, he has practiced as a retail pharmacist, outpatient clinical pharmacist, and inpatient clinical pharmacist. His current practice is as an ambulatory care clinical pharmacy specialist, where he applies his passion for lifestyle interventions in the management of chronic disease.

In addition to his career as a pharmacist, Cory is also an accomplished improv comedian, having started on his comedy journey in 2013. Since then, Cory has coached, taught, and performed improv for thousands of people. Today, Cory travels around the country speaking and teaching other healthcare professionals how to apply the valuable skills of improv comedy to create a more adaptable, empathetic, and humanizing healthcare experience.

Cory lives in Tucson, Arizona, with his wife, Cassie, their two children, and ten chickens. When he's not caring for patients or making people laugh, Cory enjoys harvesting rainwater, playing racquetball, basketball, and golf, and exploring the science of disease management through lifestyle. Cory is currently working on his master's degree in "Dad Jokes" with the help of his two sons.

I WOULD APPRECIATE YOUR FEEDBACK ON WHAT CHAPTERS HELPED YOU MOST AND WHAT YOU WOULD LIKE TO SEE IN FUTURE BOOKS.

IF YOU ENJOYED THIS BOOK AND FOUND IT HELPFUL, PLEASE LEAVE A **REVIEW** ON AMAZON.

VISIT ME AT

WWW.CORYJENKS.COM

WHERE YOU CAN SIGN UP FOR EMAIL UPDATES.

THANK YOU!

CPSIA information can be obtained
at www.ICGtesting.com
Printed in the USA
BVHW090958070222
628285BV00013B/438